HowExpert Guide to Penguins

101+ Lessons to Learn about and Love Penguins from A to Z

HowExpert with Skylar Isaac

For more tips related to this topic, visit HowExpert.com/penguins.

Recommended Resources

- HowExpert.com – Quick 'How To' Guides on All Topics from A to Z by Everyday Experts.
- HowExpert.com/free – Free HowExpert Email Newsletter.
- HowExpert.com/books – HowExpert Books
- HowExpert.com/courses – HowExpert Courses
- HowExpert.com/clothing – HowExpert Clothing
- HowExpert.com/membership – HowExpert Membership Site
- HowExpert.com/affiliates – HowExpert Affiliate Program
- HowExpert.com/jobs – HowExpert Jobs
- HowExpert.com/writers – Write About Your #1 Passion/Knowledge/Expertise & Become a HowExpert Author.
- HowExpert.com/resources – Additional HowExpert Recommended Resources
- YouTube.com/HowExpert – Subscribe to HowExpert YouTube.
- Instagram.com/HowExpert – Follow HowExpert on Instagram.
- Facebook.com/HowExpert – Follow HowExpert on Facebook.

Publisher's Foreword

Dear HowExpert Reader,

HowExpert publishes quick 'how to' guides on all topics from A to Z by everyday experts.

At HowExpert, our mission is to discover, empower, and maximize everyday people's talents to ultimately make a positive impact in the world for all topics from A to Z...one everyday expert at a time!

All of our HowExpert guides are written by everyday people just like you and me, who have a passion, knowledge, and expertise for a specific topic.

We take great pride in selecting everyday experts who have a passion, real-life experience in a topic, and excellent writing skills to teach you about the topic you are also passionate about and eager to learn.

We hope you get a lot of value from our HowExpert guides, and it can make a positive impact on your life in some way. All of our readers, including you, help us continue living our mission of positively impacting the world for all spheres of influences from A to Z.

If you enjoyed one of our HowExpert guides, then please take a moment to send us your feedback from wherever you got this book.

Thank you, and we wish you all the best in all aspects of life.

Sincerely,

BJ Min
Founder & Publisher of HowExpert
HowExpert.com

PS...If you are also interested in becoming a HowExpert author, then please visit our website at HowExpert.com/writers. Thank you & again, all the best!

Table of Contents

Introduction

This guide is all about the wonderful world of penguins. We will be learning together fun, interesting, and educational facts about penguins, from A to Z. Each chapter, lesson, and sub-lessons are fun and interesting facts. Many people may know of some of these penguin breeds but may even be taken aback while learning these exciting facts together.

Then there are penguin species that some people may have had no idea even existed. Well, we are going to learn today about the facts that I find fun and interesting. I thought I knew everything there was to know about a few of these penguins.

However, as I was writing this guide, I have found more information about the penguins I knew about, but information and interesting facts about every penguin is this guide. Ecologists study each penguin and sometimes overlook details that another ecologist will see when looking at that penguin. So, I hope you enjoy reading these 101 fun and interesting facts about penguins with me.

Chapter 1: Frequently Asked Questions

Most people who want to learn about penguins turn to google and ask many questions floating around in their heads. Here in "Frequently Asked Questions," I am going to answer some of those questions. Enjoying going through these questions, and I hope I answered all the things you wanted to know about penguins.

Lesson 1: Do All Penguins Live in the Snow?

No. Penguins do not live in nor even like the snow.

Lesson 2: So Where Do Penguins Live?

Most penguins live in either Sub-Antarctic Islands or live in warmer climates such as New Zealand, Africa, and the Galapagos Islands.

Lesson 3: Can Penguins Fly?

No. Penguins may have wings, but they are used as flippers to help them glide through the water as they swim around searching for their food.

Lesson 4: What Do Penguins Eat?

Most penguins eat krill, fish, and squid. The penguins in the colder climates mainly feed on krill to not swim very far away from land, risking becoming food to their predators.

Lesson 5: Are There Any Penguins Living in the Arctic?

No, there are not. Penguins live in the southern hemisphere, never venturing into the northern hemisphere, except for the Galapagos penguins. And even they don't venture too far into the northern hemisphere.

Lesson 6: Do Penguins Cheat on Each Other?

Most penguins are strictly monogamous and mate with one penguin for life. The only time penguins choose a new mate is when their mate dies or can't reproduce together. Cheating is usually punished by banishment from the colony.

Lesson 7: How Do Penguins Reproduce?

Penguins tend to mate for life. They have eggs when they reproduce. The eggs are then incubated, and once they hatch, they are raised by their parents.

Lesson 8: Do Penguins Have Teeth?

No, penguins do not have any teeth. They have little thorn-like structures on their tongues and throats, which keep the fish in their mouth as they swallow them whole.

Lesson 9: How Long Do Penguins Live?

It seems that most penguins can be expected to live up to 20 years old in the wild. However, when held in captivity, they tend to survive longer, getting to be as aged as 30 years old, due to the lack of predators.

Lesson 10: How Can a Penguin Drink Water?

Penguins don't drink water from the ocean. They get their needed water from the food they eat. While diving for their food, they also take in saltwater, and just like most animals, penguins cannot drink saltwater. They have a gland by their nose called the supraorbital gland, which allows the salt from the water to leave their bodies—sometimes resulting in them sneezing out the salt.

Lesson 11: Do All Penguins Glide on Their Belly?

No. Most penguins do not live in Antarctica, where the frozen icy surface allows the penguins to glide effortlessly along the surface.

Lesson 12: Can Penguins Survive in Below Freezing Temperatures?

Yes, but it does depend on the species of penguin. Take a Galapagos penguin compared to an Emperor penguin. Emperor penguins are born in Antarctica, so they can handle extremely cold weather. But if you were to pick up a Galapagos penguin and take them to Antarctica, they would more than likely freeze to death, seeing as they are born in the Galapagos Islands.

Lesson 13: What are Baby Penguins Called?

Baby penguins are often referred to as a chick. However, some may call them nestlings.

Lesson 14: What do penguins do with their dead?

Whenever a penguin is found dead, they are buried by their loved ones and friends. They dig holes using their breaks and wings, making the hole deep enough for the penguin to be put into the ground and covered up.

Lesson 15: Do Penguins Eat Their Poop?

From everything I've looked into, I can't find any proof of penguins eating their poop. The only thing I found is that the Adélie penguins eat so much krill that their poop turns pink from the pigment in the krill.

Lesson 16: Were There Penguins That Were At Least Six Feet Tall?

Yes. The "Colossus penguin," as they have been called, was a penguin that got to be six feet 8 inches tall. Their remains are the most formed fossil on record to be uncovered in Antarctica.

Lesson 17: What are Predators of Penguins?

Penguin predators include land and ocean creatures, but the most common predators are sharks, leopard seals, fur seals, and killer whales.

Lesson 18: Are penguins smart creatures?

Each penguin has its call from their ones, and even those calls are different. So yes, penguins are very intelligent creatures.

Lesson 19: What Penguins are on the Endangered Species List?

All the penguins on the endangered species list are the Yellow-eyed penguin, Erect-crested penguin, Northern Rockhopper penguin, African penguin, and the Galapagos penguins. All of these penguins have less than 160,000 penguins left in the wild.

Lesson 20: Do Penguins Get Aggressive Towards Humans?

No. Penguins tend to be quite kind to animals and humans, mainly because most penguins don't have land predators.

Lesson 21: Are Penguins Considered to be Mammals?

No, penguins are not mammals. They are birds. They hatch eggs and are covered in feathers.

Lesson 22: Can Any Penguins Jump?

Yes, technically, both of the Rockhopper penguins jump. They hop across creaks and other rocks to get to where they want to go.

Lesson 23: How Fast Can a Penguin Swim?

Most penguins swim up to 8 miles per hour, but the fastest penguin (the Gentoo penguin) swims as fast as 22 miles per hour.

Lesson 24: Are the Penguin Species Known to be Carnivores?

Yes. Penguins eat fish and no vegetation, so they are considered carnivores.

Lesson 25: Why Can't Penguins Fly?

Penguins have shorter and stiffer wings than other birds, and thus they can't fold them as other birds can. With water being thicker than air, short, stiff wings are perfect for pushing themselves through the ocean.

Also, with penguins having heavy bodies and wings built for swimming, this is the reason for them not being able to fly.

Lesson 26: Can Penguins See Colors?

Yes, penguins can see color. But as tests have shown, they only see specific colors such as violet, blue, green, and ocean colors because they rely so much on their eyesight in the water to catch their prey that they have adapted to seeing these three primary colors. Graham Martin from Britain's University of Birmingham discovered this exciting fact while conducting a color blindness test on the Humboldt penguin.

He also found out that penguins cannot see the color red as they do not need it. In the areas the penguins hunt for their food, there is no need to see red. Yes, krill is pink, but with the fact that they see blue, purple, and green, the pink krill will stand out. Besides, there isn't any coral or sponge for the krill to hide in, so not seeing red is not a problem for penguins.

Lesson 27: How Can Penguins See Underwater?

While Mr. Graham Martin conducted his color blindness test on the Humboldt penguin, he discovered that the cornea of the penguin's eyes was flatter compared to human corneas.

Having a flatter cornea helps penguins to see more clearly while submerged underwater. Seeing clearer in the ocean than humans can give penguins the benefit of spotting their prey and predators faster.

Lesson 28: What Reptiles Hunt Penguins?

Crocodiles live in the same region as penguins but do they hunt penguins? Yes, just not as the main part of their diet. Now Fairy penguins are also hunted by the reptiles called lizards, where they live. And Galapagos penguins are hunted on land by snakes.

Lesson 29: Are Penguins Nocturnal?

Yes, penguins can be nocturnal. The only penguin to be nocturnal are the Little Blue/Fairy penguins. They are nocturnal to protect themselves from the on-land predators. They stay in the water all day long from dusk till dawn, only coming onshore at night to rest and feed their chicks.

Lesson 30: What are Five Fun Facts to Learn about Penguins?

While this is a good question, it is also a tricky question. What I found to be interesting and fun facts may not be that interesting to others. So, I will list five new points that I find interesting.

-Penguins can't see the color red.

-A Rice Rat can hunt Galapagos penguins.

-Penguins do not have teeth; they have pointy little thorn-like structures on their tongues that lead into their throats that help the fish go down whole.

-Every breed of penguins is strictly monogamous though there are some exceptions. The death of one's mate and not being able to reproduce with each other are two exceptions to penguins being monogamous. Emperor penguin females may even cheat on their mate for no apparent reason while on her four-month fishing trip.

-Only two penguin species hold their egg on their feet: the King and Emperor male penguins.

Lesson 31: Can I Keep a Penguin as a Pet in my House?

No, you cannot keep a penguin as a pet. Living in the United States of America, it is considered illegal to have a penguin as a pet. But you cannot have a pet penguin because there are no penguin breeders, and if you only want one penguin, it would be a very lonely pet, so more than one is needed.

All penguin species are social birds, so they feel much more comfortable living in a pack or colony as they are called for penguins. So, if you plan on having a penguin as a pet, you will need to buy not just one but at least 20 penguins, so they have the comfort of being in a colony of their own with their friends and family.

Lesson 32: Is There a Zoo That Allows You to Pet and Interact with Penguins?

Yes, there is a zoo where you can go and interact with penguins. At the Maryland zoo in Baltimore, they allow their visitors to pet the African penguins they have. There is a fee of 50 US dollars but paying for this feature allows you to speak with the zookeepers and pet the penguins during what they call a "behind-the-scenes" tour of the new, well newer, penguin habitat enclosure.

Lesson 33: Are There Any Penguin Video Games?

There are a few penguins in video games. And a few video games with penguins being the character. Most of them are outdated, like the online web game that I'm sure many children have played called Club Penguin. Then there are penguins inside of other video games like the game Spyro.

Lesson 34: Is There a Sports Team Named the Penguins?

Yes, there is, and they are called the Pittsburgh Penguins. They are a hockey team in the United States of America.

Lesson 35: What is the Oldest Penguin Species?

The oldest penguin to have existed but is now extinct is the Waimanu manneringi penguin. This penguin existed in the Paleocene period, not too long after the Cretaceous-Paleocene extinction event. Believing this penguin lived among the dinosaurs supports the theory that flightless birds existed before and after the dinosaurs' extinction. Even though the Waimanu could not fly, they also didn't have the same bone structure in their wings that penguin species have nowadays. This meaning that they most likely did not partake in the aquatic lifestyle we see from penguins now.

Lesson 36: Why are Penguins Black and White?

Penguins are black and white due to their plumage as adults being black and white. However, the black and white coloration's reason and usefulness are that it works as camouflage while in the water. This type of camouflage is called countershading. Countershading means that with the two colors on the penguins, they can blend into their surroundings. Those surroundings happen to be in the ocean.

Their backs' black coloration helps them blend into the ocean floor as light penetration does not reach to the bottom of the ocean in every place on the ocean, allowing them to hide in plain sight. Now, as for the white coloration, this is so that sharks and other predators from below the penguin can look up to where they hear or feel a penguin and be led astray as the sunlight cause the penguin to blend in using their white stomachs as an empty canvas mixing in with the light of the sun.

Lesson 37: What are the Most Widespread Penguins in the World?

The southern rockhopper penguins of just the rockhopper penguin species, in general, are the most widespread in the world. Though roughly two-thirds of the almost 2 million southern rockhopper population that breed on the Falkland Islands belongs to the Eudyptes chrysocome species.

Lesson 38: Do Penguins Cry?

No, penguins do not cry. They do, however, secrete salt from their eyes and nose.

Lesson 39: Do Penguins Eat Carrots?

No, penguins do not eat carrots. This is for a few reasons; they have no teeth, and carrots do not grow around where penguins live.

Chapter 2: Life Cycle of a Penguin

The life cycle of a penguin is exactly what it sounds like; the breakdown and explanation of a penguin's life cycle. In this chapter, we will be breaking down the life cycle of penguins into four lessons. Lesson one will be from incubation to nestling, though this lesson may be shorter than the next three lessons as incubation is typically pretty quick.

The next lesson will be the cycle of nestling to fledgling, and we will find out together what a fledgling penguin is. Lesson three will be about the fledgling penguins becoming an adult penguin. And finally, the last lesson is about adult penguins to death and what is don't with their dead loved ones.

Lesson 40: Incubation to Nestling

The period from incubation to nestling is typically a quick process lasting for around 45 to a little over 65 days. During the incubation period, both the male and female penguins will usually take care of the nesting eggs. There are two species of penguins that only the male will take care of just one egg while the female goes foraging for food.

Each parent penguin takes turns watching over the clutch of eggs. Each pair could have at least two eggs per clutch. Penguins can lay more than two eggs per clutch, but for all the research I have personally done, it is rare for there to be more than two eggs at a time.

It is also possible for breeding penguins to have two clutches during a single breeding period. However, this is unlikely as well, usually unless the first clutch fails. Now, after incubation comes the nestlings.

It is simple to explain what a nestling is; they are the newborn penguins, also referred to as chicks. After both being cared for by either the parents or just the father penguin, when the egg hatches, it is usually the father with the chick or chicks.

The father is left with the clutch during hatching because the female penguins will be out foraging for the upcoming chick arriving soon. How the male and female penguins detect that their egg or eggs are about to hatch is unknown to me, seeing as how while researching everything I could about penguins, I could not find that piece of information that I was missing.

It is most likely that because eggs need to be incubated during the incubation period for them to survive, scientists and researchers have not figured out how the parents can often tell when the mother should go foraging. So, with that being said, after the mother returns for her fishing trip, she will then feed the chick who has either just hatched or has been hatched for a few hours.

If two eggs need to hatch, the first penguin chick to hatch is not fed until the second one hatches. Therefore, usually is the one chick that passes away, mainly due to having to wait to feed and not being adequately cared for during that time. They are also often the smaller of the two eggs to start with. Though they get the same amount of heat, it is unlikely to survive because they do not get the proper care during the two to five days it could take for the second egg to hatch.

Lesson 41: Nestling to Fledgling

Nestlings are the chicks that are cared for after hatching if there are two eggs in a single clutch; usually, the second chick is the one to survive. With that being said and explained, let us move one and discuss the cycle of nestling to fledging. We will also discuss and learn about what precisely a penguin fledgling is.

From the time they are born, penguins are taken care of by their parents until they reach a certain age. When the penguin chick hatches, they are fed as soon as their mother returns from her fishing trip. If there are two eggs in a clutch, then even if the female penguin returns to one of her chicks hatched, she waits for the second chick to hatch before feeding either one.

During the hatching process involving two eggs, the second egg usually hatches two to five days after the first egg. So, having to wait to be fed for that long period, especially if it takes five days for the second egg to hatch, the first chick will be lucky to survive once finally being fed.

Having not been fed or truly cared for by its parent penguin while waiting for the second egg to hatch, the first nestling usually dies, but there are times when the breeding pair will take care of both penguins. Taking care of both parents' chicks ensures that at least one nestling will survive into adulthood, let alone the fledgling phase.

During the fledgling phase of a penguin's life cycle, they start to go through changes like humans go through puberty (only we cannot fend for ourselves after only 11 weeks of life). Yep, you read that correctly; some penguins can begin their own life's journey after as few as 11 weeks of birth.

There is a timeline that a penguin can be independent enough to leave the nest for good, and that is typically between the ages of 11 weeks to even 100 days old. After spending at least 30 days in the nest being taken care of by both their mother and father penguin, they join a group what is called a crèche.

They form these groups to be protected while all the parent penguins are out fishing. Older penguins and those who did not have a successful clutch that season stay with the crèche groups to keep them safe from predators.

So, nestlings are the newborn chicks. So what is the definition of penguin fledglings? The true definition of a fledgling is usually when a bird is old enough to leave the nest but has not learned to fly yet because they have not grown their flight feathers yet. But as we know with penguins, they do not fly.

With learning the definition of a fledgling now, we should think about what that could mean for a penguin. No, penguins cannot fly, but they do have feathers that are their adult feathers. Understanding this means that while penguins are being considered as fledglings, they will start molting their juvenile feathers and grow in their adult ones.

And yes, they leave the nest during the beginning of this phase to join a group of other juvenile penguins while their parents go fishing. The parents come back every night to feed their chick or chicks, and then they leave every morning to gather more food.

Once the fledgling penguins reach between 11 weeks to 100 days, they start to molt their juvenile feathers and grow into their adult feathers. Before this period though their parents have taught them everything, they need to know about surviving independently. They even join their parents in foraging for food after the 30 days that their parents leave them with the crèches is over until they have reached the age to be completely independent and own their own.

Lesson 42: Fledgling to Adult

Now, this next phase is about the fledgling turning into an adult. While we discussed the fledgling previously, going from nestling to fledging is different. Yes, we talk about some of the same information about fledglings, but we will also talk about how they transition into adults.

Fledglings are the penguins who have not lost their juvenile plumage yet are still independent enough to live in crèches with other juvenile penguins. They are still cared for by their parents every night. After 30 days of living in their chosen crèches during the day and coming back to the nest at night, they can join their parents.

Joining their parents means that the mother and father penguins take their chicks on fishing trips. They go on these fishing trips with their parents to learn how to forage for their food. When they learn how to fish by being taught by their parents, they are also taught other things they need to survive independently.

Male and female penguins teach their fledgling penguins about predators and how to get away from them. Penguins can swim at high speeds when needed, so while in the water, if a predator is coming and if the penguin has the advantage of seeing them ahead of time, they can speed out of the water.

They can also use their speed to catch fish faster and mess around in the water by leaping out of the water somewhat like a dolphin, just not as high. Not only do fledglings learn about how to survive independently, but they also learn about how to have fun in the water. Being in the water makes up at least 75 percent of a penguin's life.

When the fledglings begin to lose their juvenile plumage, this is called molting. During the molting period, the juvenile feathers are replaced with adult feathers. This process takes at least four weeks to complete. So, during those four weeks, the penguins are unable to enter the water. They are no longer waterproof while molting, so they are stranded on land until the new feathers completely grow in.

Being waterproof is protection for penguins. No, they cannot fly, so why should they be waterproof, you ask? Well, let's think about that for a second. Penguins do not fly, yet they have feathers and wings that become waterproof. However, other species of birds have wings, feathers, and fly, but they do not get to be waterproof; that doesn't seem to be very fair.

Now let's think that most bird species do not depend on their survival on being in the water. Penguins do rely solely on what they get from the ocean to survive. Being in the Antarctic region, penguins need to be waterproof. To have that freezing ocean water run off their feathers instead of soaking them through to their skin.

If the water didn't drop off the penguins, they would freeze to death due to freezing water and winds mixed with snow and ice on the ground. Penguins would have died out a long time ago if they were never waterproof. So, having discussed that the adult and juvenile penguins are both waterproof, but when they go through their molting period, they have to stay on land to not freeze to death.

Another thing you may be wondering is, how do they survive going four weeks without eating? Well, penguins know when their feathers are getting old and about to go through their molting phase. This is because they molt once a year around the same time each year. The time of molting may differ from juvenile to adult, but it's always the same once they are adults.

With that being said, for them to know when they are about to molt, which is usually February for juvenile penguins and March or April for the adult penguins. Penguins will then eat extra the entire month before molting to gain extra fat, so they do not starve while molting.

When juvenile penguins are done molting and have all of their adult feathers, they are no longer considered juvenile, especially if they had learned to be independent by the time they were supposed to and have their adult feathers. Once this happens, they are usually bigger by now and do not look like baby penguins, so they have become adult penguins by this point in time.

Lesson 43: Adult to Death

There is more than one way for a penguin to die, just as there is more than one way for humans to die. They can die due to old age, predator attacks, random plagues and illnesses, human interference, and natural effects like the ocean's fluctuating temperatures, causing their food sources to travel further out.

After penguins get their adult feathers and have learned how to thrive independently, they leave with the breeding colony to go to either the same habitat as their parents or choose a new one. Once they leave the breeding grounds, newly aged adult penguins do not return to the breeding grounds until they have come of age to mate.

The typical age for penguins to begin mating starts with the female penguins maturing first by around three years old. The male penguins do not become sexually mature until they are at least four or five years of age. Once both male and female penguins are sexually mature, they can then choose who to mate with.

Now almost every species of penguin is strictly monogamous, meaning they mate for life. A penguin pair will not continue mating because they cannot reproduce together, and another reason is if they can produce eggs together, but the clutch fails.

A penguin doesn't stay monogamous if their partner dies from natural causes, illness, or predators. Even there are some female penguins that after mating and laying an egg with a male penguin, while he takes care of the egg, she may find a new mate on her fishing trip.

It is very rare for penguins to go against their monogamous nature, though when they do, if it is not mutual between a penguin pair to leave each other, then it is considered cheating, the same as humans. Though the difference between when penguins cheat on their spouse, they are punished. Being punished in a penguin community means that the cheating pair of penguins are usually banished from the colony.

With that being said, penguins cheating on one another is usually rare. After penguins reach their sexual maturity, they go to the breeding colonies and find their forever mate. When they find their forever mate, they begin preparations on making a nest for the soon to be egg or eggs.

They spend at least 75 percent of their lives in the ocean eating and just swimming around enjoying the water. The diet of penguins is mostly all the same, seeing as they all live around the same area. Most penguins live in the Antarctic region, and some even live near Africa and areas near there.

The adult to death part of a penguins' life is pretty much on repeat. They molt every year at the same time, breed every year at the same (even if each breed has a different month they breed in), some even migrate at the same time every year, and they spend most of the daytime every day in the water getting food for themselves, nestlings, and possibly their mate.

Penguins also eat the same food every day when they go fishing. This cycle repeats every day and every year for the rest of their lives until they either pass away or are hunted by one of the many predators they have. Humans have also been known as predators to almost every species of penguins. It is believed that people used to hunt penguins as a source of food while on long expositions or to be able to survive if they were outcast or stranded. People hunted penguins for the oil that they secrete from their pores that make the penguin's waterproof feathers.

After a long (hopefully) healthy life, most penguins are lucky to live to be up to the age of 29 years old. With having predators, illnesses, and humans to worry about, the age a penguin dying varies. Though the longest a penguin has been recorded to live in the wild is around 29 years old.

Chapter Review

In this chapter, the lessons teach about individual stages in a penguin's life, and each stage can have a fine point pulled out to explain its importance easily.

The first point or fun fact I found in this chapter is about the incubation into the nestling stage of a penguins' life. When it comes time for incubation, the adult penguins make nests to put the eggs in. The interesting part about the incubation to nestling stage of a penguins' life cycle is the fact that in almost every penguin species, except for two of them, both male and female penguins take care of the clutch.

A second fun fact or point is coming from the nestling to the fledgling cycle of life. I find it interesting because when penguins go from nestlings to fledglings, they have time for them to become completely independent. That period starts from the 30 days after the parents take turns caring for the nestlings.

When the nestlings leave the nest, they join other penguins groups, which start their period for becoming completely independent. It usually takes 30 to 100 days for a nestling to become fully grown into a fledgling. Once they are fledglings, then they can go with their parents during that time.

My third point from this chapter is from the fledgling to adult lesson. The fact is that when a fledgling becomes an adult penguin, they molt their juvenile feathers and grow their adult feather in a month. Some of the penguin species have brown and dirty looking feathers when they begin molting, which then grow into fresh black, dark blue, or blue-black adult feathers.

The fourth and final fact from this chapter that I think is important, if not interesting, is that while penguins have no clue if they will survive the day, let alone the year, they are monogamous breeders. They stay faithful to the one mate they've chosen, and it is almost always for life. I know some humans who can't stay with a person for a few months, let alone their whole life.

Penguins only ever change partners due to three reasons (mainly the first two as the last one doesn't happen often). Reason number one is due to one of the penguins dying either from natural causes or from a predator. The second reason penguins would have to change partners is because they are not compatible and did not reproduce any offspring. The third reason is a pretty rare occurrence, though it does happen, which is if one of the mates' cheat with another penguin (mated or not).

Chapter 3: Everyday People and Penguins

In this chapter, we will be talking about everyday people and penguins. The few things I will be going over in this chapter are, can penguins be owned as pets, are there penguins in zoos, can people interact with penguins at zoos, and are there ways to see penguins in the wild.

Lesson 44: Can Penguins be Owned as Pets?

Most everyday people don't dream of owning a penguin, and this is for a good reason, owning just one penguin would never work because these birds are what I like to call "pack" birds, which means that for a penguin to thrive, they need to belong in a group or "pack" of penguins.

That also means that a person wanting to own a penguin has to buy several penguins at one time, several as in at least two to six penguins. However, penguins are more comfortable in groups with higher numbers. They tend to be social butterflies and like to be in a group of at least 20 penguins though this is in the wild where they need their strength in numbers.

However, if you live in the USA, you may not own a penguin in any amount as it is illegal. Due to many of the penguin species not having many penguins left, with some penguins species even being endangered, under the Endangered Species Act, owning any penguin is against the law.

Besides, owning a penguin, let alone two or six penguins, could get very expensive. The cost for one penguin is up to 20,000 United States Dollars. And I'd hope it comes without saying, but you'll need a male and a female penguin if you were only to purchase two. So, in answering the discussion topic, "can penguins be owned as pets?" no, penguins cannot be owned as pets legally, at least not in the U.S.

Lesson 45: Are There Penguins in Zoos?

To make the answer short and sweet, yes, there are penguins in zoos. Every zoo? No, penguins are not in every zoo, and most zoos only have one species of penguin. Take the San Francisco Zoo in San Francisco, California. For instance, they have penguins but they only Blackfoot penguins there.

There are at least thirteen zoos with enclosures for penguins in the U.S. alone, and each zoo has one or more penguins species. Penguins also live in aquariums around the U.S. So far, there are only four aquariums in the U.S.; two houses one breed of penguin, and the other two aquariums houses two breeds of penguin each.

The U.S.'s zoos are in the following states: California, Illinois, Missouri, Michigan, Nebraska, New York,

Oklahoma, Pennsylvania, Tennessee, Texas, and Wisconsin. The four aquariums in the United States are in Massachusetts, Illinois, and two in California.

Australia has two zoos and one aquarium. The zoos are in Sydney and Melbourne, while the aquarium is also in Melbourne. There is also a penguin parade in Australia every night in Melbourne, and I mention this because while driving to this penguin parade, Fairy penguins can be seen at the Phillip Island Nature Park.

Another place I was able to find zoos that have enclosures for penguins is in the U.K. There are two zoos in the United Kingdom, one in Bristol, England, and the other zoo is in Edinburgh, Scotland.

Each zoo from all and the world had different types and amounts of penguins. An example is that a zoo in Missouri has four penguin breeds, and they are King, Gentoo, Rockhopper, and Humboldt penguins. At the same time, the zoo in Sydney, Australia, has Fairy penguins. Blackfoot Penguins are in the U.K. zoo located in Bristol, England.

Lesson 46: Can people Interact with Penguins at the Zoo?

The next lesson we will be covering is, "can people interact with penguins at the zoo?". Now that is a good question; it's also something I am curious about. So, let us dive into the zoo world and see what we can find about interacting with penguins.

Usually, people are not allowed into enclosures with the animals due to unforeseen consequences that could occur, just like when that poor child fell into Harambe's habitat at the Cincinnati Zoo in Cincinnati, Ohio, U.S. I know we can't compare gorillas to penguins, but that doesn't mean the same thing couldn't happen.

When the toddler fell into Harambe's cage, everyone freaked out, not knowing what Harambe would do. Then he started to drag the poor child around in the moot, so the zookeepers had to do something and quickly. Yes, shooting to kill an endangered species may not have been the smartest choice, but it was the quickest way to save the child.

The same thing could happen with any animal, even if they are raised in the zoo around people every day. A wild animal is always going to be unpredictable. And yes, I believe the same goes for penguins. If they feel threatened, they will attack whatever is threatening them.

Heading back to this lesson's topic, there is a zoo where people can interact with penguins for a fee. That fee is 49 USD for zoo members and 59 USD for non-members. The zoo is called the Maryland Zoo located in Baltimore, Maryland, U.S.

The penguins that they have are African penguins. The tours for the "meet and greet," as they call it, are between 20 minutes and 30 minutes. Only one ticket per person and the age is five and older. With the age requirement being at five or older is a sign that younger children may scream or be loud on accident, and the penguins may react in a way the zoo does not want, especially during a tour of being able to pet and take pictures with these penguins.

There are more requirements to have a penguin encounter at the Maryland Zoo, including pay for zoo admission. Going to a zoo and having a show encounter with any penguin would be very impressive.

Lesson 47: Are There Ways to See Penguins in the Wild?

In this lesson, we will learn if it is possible to see penguins in the wild. Due to the endangered species act, it is hard to know which animals you will see in the wild without breaking the law. Luckily, we have the internet and can find ways to legally see animals in the wild and hopefully in person.

So, as I mentioned in lesson 6, "are there penguins in zoos?" there is a spot in Australia to see fairy penguins in the wild. That is at the Phillip Island Nature Park on your way to the penguin parade held every night. However, there are also other places to see penguins in their natural habitat.

There are six other places you can see penguins in the wild; one of the six places is the Galapagos Islands. The Galapagos Islands are located in Ecuador, and the island that you can see the Galapagos is Bartolome Island. Another two islands that Galapagos penguins can be seen are the Isabela and Fernandina islands.

On the Ballestas Islands in Peru, taking a boat ride around this will give you a great view of the Humboldt penguins. They are usually lining the rocky coastline. Getting to the Ballestas Islands takes a four-hour drive to Paracas, Peru, from Peru's capital Lima. You then take a boat ride around the islands and enjoy the view of all those Humboldt penguins.

Going to a fourth area, penguins can be seen in the wild is a reserve located in Punta Tombo, Argentina. The reserve is called Punta Tombo National Reserve. Due to how many Magellanic penguins come to the reserve to nest during their breeding season, this place was nicknamed "penguin paradise."

The Falkland Islands is one more place to see penguins thriving naturally. However, land mines are scattered across the Yorkey Bay area from the 10-week war of the Falklands. The areas where there are land mines have been fenced off so that it is safe for humans to view.

Gentoo and Magellanic penguins live here, and since they did weigh enough to trigger the land mines, they have not only survived living here, but they have thrived and most likely grown in numbers. I say this because they have been left untouched by humans since 1982.

Boulders Beach in South Africa is one more place that penguins can be found. Only in this place, the penguins seem to be interested in people's cars. The penguins residing here are the African penguins, and they enjoy their spot on the beach and even wander off into the parking lot with all the cars.

The seventh and final place (that I can find anyway) is Martillo Island. Located in Argentina, Martillo Island is also known as the "penguin island" because of the amount of Magellanic and gentoo penguins that form breeding colonies here. As many as 1,000 penguin nests can be found during the breeding seasons.

Chapter Review

In this chapter, the lessons I found interesting are:

- There are plenty of zoos to choose from to see penguins.
- There are places where you can see penguins in their natural habitat.
- You can even interact with penguins at a zoo, and the last fact I found interesting from this chapter is that if it was legal to own a penguin in the U.S., they could cost up to 20,000 USD.

One fact I find to be interesting is that there are plenty of zoos that have penguins to choose from to visit. The U.S. has at least thirteen zoos that have penguin enclosures. And that's not even counting the aquariums that house penguins in the U.S.

Other countries have zoos and aquariums for penguins to live there and be visited by humans, even if most of them stay beyond barriers. My second fact, which has to do with seeing penguins at the zoo, is you can interact with penguins on a "meet and greet" tour. However, I could only find one zoo that offers this, and the zoo is in the state of Maryland in the United States.

The Maryland Zoo allows you to encounter African penguins on their tour behind the scenes. Of course, you have to pay to get into the "meet and greet" tour, apart from the admissions fee to get into the zoo. When planning to go on the tour, there are regulations one must meet before buying the tickets, such as an age restriction.

Another interesting fact from this chapter is there are other chances for people to see penguins even if there are no zoos with them near you. There are natural habitats where penguins either live or migrate to for their breeding seasons. Finding these places allows you to see how a penguin indeed acts in nature.

Some of the locations may be hard to get to, but in the end, it'll be worth it to see a penguin genuinely enjoy their life and not be stuck in a cage, especially if they've been inside that cage or "enclosure" all of their life. I know zoos and aquariums have these enclosures to preserve as many of the penguin species as possible, but I still believe a penguin would be happier being free.

Another lesson that I find to be interesting from this chapter is that if it were legal to own penguins in the U.S., they would cost up to 20,000 USD each, and that's just for buying the penguins. That doesn't include the cost amount in the food they would need in a year, which could be 1,000 USD or more per penguin. It all depends on which fish is bought for the penguins to eat.

You also have to consider that you would need to get an exotic animal license to be able even to keep the penguins. You would also need to get checkups done, probably at a zoo, which could be expensive. Maybe owning at least two penguins (you need a male and female penguin) doesn't sound so easy anymore.

Take owning two penguins; for instance, you would need a lot of knowledge to obtain and maintain two penguins' lives. As I discussed the facts that interested me the most, I realized I enjoy helping people learn and understand new information that they may have never known.

Maybe I even gave someone a new way of looking at the information they already know about penguins. The next chapter of this guide will be about fun facts I found while learning more about penguins myself. Doing research helps pick out points from articles that I have never heard about penguins, and I brought them into this guide because I think other penguin enthusiasts like myself would like to hear more fun facts about penguins.

Chapter 4: Penguin Fun Facts

Lesson 48: Penguin Fun Facts

There are many things to learn about penguins; some can be funny, some sound weird and crazy, some might even sound false, but researchers have taken a long time to study penguins. Once ecologists release their study data, some people tend to separate the information into smaller articles, broken down into categories. Categories such as how many breeds of penguins there are, how they take care of the nest and chicks, and sometimes every detail found about one or all penguins are broken down into group articles.

The first fun fact about penguins that I love is the fact that there is a blue penguin. I grew up as most people probably did, never knowing that there is a penguin species that is blue. They aren't bright blue; they are mostly dark blue. Looking at them from a distance, you probably couldn't tell they are blue; they would look shiny.

These penguins are not taught about in school when kids are being taught about endangered species, plants, and animal science. At least that's how it was where I'm from. We landed about endangered species as a whole, meaning we were told penguins as the whole species were endangered; they still are, but we never learned about each breed as the individual breeds that they are.

During environmental science, the only time any student learned about even just one penguin species is when we watched an educational movie about animals and the environment of the Galapagos islands. When learning about the Galapagos islands, I learned about the penguins that live there; no, the video wasn't about the penguins in general, so we didn't learn much about them.

A second fun fact about penguins is penguins drink saltwater while almost no other land animal can. They have special glands around their nose and sometimes their eyes that allow salt from the saltwater to be secreted from their bodies when they swallow fish and water. This will enable penguins to stay hydrated because water and food are the primary sources of survival.

Fun fact number three that I just learned and think is pretty cool is that a group of penguins in the water is called a raft. Yes, like a pool raft; I think that is cool because even though they are called that in the water, they look nothing like a floating raft. A fourth fact that goes along with fact number three is a group of penguins called a raft while in water is called a waddle while on land.

Interestingly, penguins are called rafts and waddles; I only knew they belonged in colonies. I assumed that was the name for a group of penguins. Now I know they have two names. I knew that other animals had names for their groups, though I guess I just never thought that for penguins.

Many facts break down from study research articles and make it into fun fact lists for everyday readers to learn about penguins without reading about the statistics between the points or before the exciting facts that people want to know.

My fifth chosen fact about penguins is that they do not have teeth. The way they eat is they swallow the fish whole, and they have pointy little spines lining their tongue and back of their throat to keep the fish in their mouth and help it go down.

When explorers first spotted penguins, the explorers called them strange geese; this is fun fact number six. These explorers were circumnavigating the Falkland Islands when they noticed these penguins. The seventh fact has to do with penguins from fact number six: these penguins are now most likely known as the Magellanic penguins.

Another fun fact, fact eight, is that female emperor penguins tend to choose the chunkier, fluffier male penguins to mate with due to the fact they can go for a long period without food. Going more extended periods without food is a benefit for the male penguins just in case their mate is late coming back from her fishing trip or even if she does not return at all.

The ninth fun fact about penguins is that scientists can find colonies of penguins from outer space using photographs tracking the amount of penguin guano in a particular spot at a specific time. My tenth and final fun fact for this chapter is that in 2018 using the guano photos from space research, there were 1.5 million individual Adélie penguins found on an island called the Danger Islands.

Chapter Review

My review for this chapter will include four lessons chosen at random from the chapter that I find fun or educationally interesting. These four lessons are:

1) penguin guano can be seen from space

2) explorers once referred to penguins as strange geese

3) there is a blue penguin

4) when a group of penguins is on land, they are called a waddle.

Facts that I chose to review from this chapter intrigue me the most due to their uniqueness. The first fact I picked out is that space stations can see penguin guano from space. This seems interesting because other animals cannot be tracked this way. Also, being able to track penguins like this could help find where more might be at and see if humans as a race can stop or slow down the extinction of penguins and possibly other animals.

The second fact I have picked from this chapter is explorers once calling penguins strange geese, even Magellanic penguins. It is intriguing to me that explorers would call any penguin a goose because they cannot fly. Then I think about how they may not have stayed around long enough to see if they would fly; these explorers were circumnavigating after all.

The third fact chosen is that there is a blue penguin. I love this because I would never have guessed my wild imagination as a child growing up loving penguins that there could be a blue one. These blue ones are also very small penguins. Many penguin lovers have wanted to see one in person (myself included) after finding out about them.

My fourth and final fact from this chapter is that a waddle of penguins is a group of penguins on land. Calling a group of penguins on land a waddle is funny because that is also how they walk. They can also be called a rookery, but it doesn't sound as funny.

One additional fact that I found to be the most interesting is, penguin guano can be seen even from space in photos.

Chapter 5: Breeding Patterns of Penguins

Just like every penguin is different, the breeding habits of penguins are different as well. Each penguin species has its way of breeding and looking for a mate. These habits could even seem similar to another penguin's breeding pattern but have the slightest bit of difference. Their breeding seasons are during different months throughout the year. A few penguins that I picked to go over their breeding patterns are the Emperor penguin, the Fairy penguin, the Macaroni penguin, and the Chinstrap penguin.

Lesson 49: The Breeding Patterns of the Emperor Penguins

Ecologists have studied the breeding patterns of the Emperor penguins for months, even years at a time, to learn and understand Emperor penguins' patterns. I would love to study and watch penguins to determine their habits be it breeding patterns or any other habits they have. I think it would be peaceful.

Emperor penguins tend to be monogamous, but they don't typically mate for life. The female Emperor penguin leaves her egg with the male penguin while she gathers food for the hatchling and maybe even her mate. Though sometimes, the female penguins may not make it back due to mainly two reasons. One reason is they are attacked and killed by predators. The second reason is that they find a new mate and leave the other mate behind while taking care of the hatchling on their own.

They breed from March through to April, with female Emperor penguins laying one egg during May. She then transfers the egg to her mated partner, who takes care of the egg for the entire incubation period. The female penguin leaves for a little over two months for her fishing period to bring food back for when the young penguin hatches.

Lesson 50: The Breeding Patterns of the Fairy Penguins

The breeding patterns of the Fairy penguins are relatively simple, seeing as they have a short lifespan. Fairy penguins tend to breed from June through to December but vary in different parts of the country. They are monogamous breeders staying with the same partner for years. The Fairy penguins' separation rate is around 18%, meaning that they tend not to choose other partners.

Female Fairy penguins usually only lay one clutch of eggs during their breeding cycle. But they can lay two if they fail to lay one during the more preferred, or usual, egg-laying time. These penguins separate because they can't reproduce with each other and have to choose a new mate. They can also separate if one of the mates passes away by old age or being killed by a predator.

During the beginning of the breeding season, the male and female penguins will burrow a spot to put their eggs for the incubation period. The male Fairy penguin is usually the one that does most of the work digging into the ground. The average depth they dig into the ground is 1 foot and 3.7 inches.

Lesson 51: The Breeding Patterns of the Macaroni Penguins

Macaroni penguins breeding season begins during October, with the females laying two eggs at the beginning of November. Even though the female Macaroni penguin will produce two eggs, typically, only one egg will survive. Male and female Macaroni penguins incubate their eggs in shifts.

When one penguin sits on the eggs, the other penguin will go fishing so that they can eat and take a break from sitting on the egg all day for a few days in a row. The incubation of the eggs takes about 33 to 37 days. When the young penguins hatch, whichever one of the parent penguins are out gathering food will have to make sure to bring extra for the hatchling.

Lesson 52: The Breeding Patterns of the Chinstrap Penguins

The breeding season for the Chinstrap penguin starts in November and ends in March. Both parents will take turns sitting on the egg to incubate it. They typically lay two eggs with only one surviving. Their eggs are creamy white, and I would say that to me, based on pictures from the National Geographic and New Zealand birds' websites, the Chinstrap penguin egg is likely the same shape as a chicken's egg.

The size of the Chinstrap penguin egg is 2.6 inches in length and 2.0 inches in width. In comparison, a large chicken egg is usually around 2.1 inches in length and 1.6 inches in width. The times that the female Chinstrap penguin will lay her eggs are as early as November and December. The incubation period will last for a maximum of 40 days.

The cause of only one hatchling surviving is that they are laid at least 2-4 days apart, so the egg that hatches first will have already eaten and been cared for longer and better than the second hatchling if it even gets the chance to be incubated and kicked from the nest. The incubation period being short makes sense seeing as the Chinstrap penguins tend to survive in the wild for an average of 16 years. Though there has been recorded of Chinstrap surviving up to 20 years old in the wild.

Chapter Review

In this chapter review, I will go over five facts about penguin breeding that I found interesting. One fact that I find interesting, yet morally wrong to me, is the fact that the female Emperor penguins could sometimes choose to mate with another penguin after already having an egg and mate waiting for her return. Now, this is rare, but it does happen.

The second fact that I found to be interesting is that most penguins are monogamous. I knew that penguins mated to have eggs, but I found out that penguins are usually a strictly monogamous species after knowing (for years) that Emperor females may choose another mate. The third fact that is interesting to me about penguins' breeding patterns is that they each have their months for them to breed in, even if they overlap other penguin breeding times.

Fact number four that is interesting is that almost every penguin lays at least two eggs, except for the Emperor and King penguins, with each of them only laying one egg per breeding season. And the final fact I find interesting about penguins' breeding patterns is that most penguins take turns incubating their eggs.

Chapter 6: How Penguins Keep Their Eggs

In this chapter, we will be learning about the different ways a select few penguins keep their eggs. While I believed that penguins carried their eggs around on their feet, I was surprised to find out that this fact was not true for all penguins. For the most part, penguins make nests much as other birds do, only not in trees.

What they use for the nest is quite different, even between each penguin species. There are three ways I found that penguins keep their eggs. One way is carrying them on their feet; yes, it's true, just not for all penguins. A second way is that they make their nests using a few different things. The third way that penguins keep their eggs is to dig holes for them or put them in the ground's crevasses.

Lesson 53: Some Penguins Carry Their Eggs on their Feet

Two penguin species carry their egg on their feet, and they are the Emperor and King penguins. Each of these penguin species only lay one egg. The male penguins are the ones to carry the eggs.

Lesson 54: The Emperor Penguins

The male Emperor penguins carry the egg on their feet. They do this due to living in Antarctica. They incubate the egg using their brood pouch. The brood pouch is a spot right above their feet where the egg is kept underneath them. With the egg being kept underneath the male Emperor penguins brood pouch, the egg is safe and warm. The incubation period of an Emperor penguin egg is 65-75 days. During the summer, the male penguin has to store enough body fat to survive the long and sometimes harsh winters.

Lesson 55: The King Penguins

King penguins also have a brood pouch. Seeing as they are closely related to the Emperor penguins, they tend to keep their eggs warm in the same manner. And again, it is only the male King penguins that carry the egg on their feet. Thus, keeping the egg safe from danger and warm enough to incubate.

The period of incubation for the King penguins' egg is 54 days. The King penguins are very territorial, especially when it comes to protecting their egg, more so than the Emperor penguin. And just like their cousin penguin, the Emperor penguin, King penguins store body fat to survive winter while incubating their egg in their brood pouch.

Lesson 56: Some Penguins Make Nests to Sit on Their Eggs

While some penguins carry their eggs on their feet, some penguins sit on their egg just like other species of birds. To name two of these penguins that sit on their eggs are the Chinstrap penguin and the Gentoo penguin. These two penguins spend the egg incubation period sitting on their egg as their partner leaves to gather food for them.

Lesson 57: The Chinstrap Penguins

Chinstrap penguins tend to keep their eggs in a nest that they make. They don't have many things to make their nests within their surrounding environment. So, they use the things they can find. The material usually always used by the Chinstrap penguin to form their nest is stones.

Also, while their breeding colonies tend to be large in number, the amount of stones available in that area tends to be low. With stones being almost rare in Chinstrap penguins' breeding grounds, they tend to steal stones from their fellow neighbor penguins to make their own nest.

Lesson 58: The Gentoo Penguins

The same thing goes for the Gentoo penguins. They use stones to build their nests as it is the only thing they can find in their neighborhood. The Gentoo male penguins can gain favor with a female if they bring her a better stone than the ones she may already have.

Doing so pairs them if she accepts the stone. Gentoo male penguins either steal stones from other nests, penguins, or find the best stone hidden away surrounding their breeding area. Other things may help keep the eggs warm such as grass, leaves, and sticks if they can be found.

Lesson 59: Some Penguins Put Their Eggs in Between Rocks, Crevices, or Burrows

Other penguins will put their eggs in crevices, in burrows, underneath tree roots, or in caves to keep them protected. This protects the eggs from either being eaten by predators or being cooked in the sun. Two of the penguins that do this are the Galapagos penguin and the African penguin. Yes, they still sit on the egg clutch if they choose to make a nest instead of putting the egg in a burrow.

Lesson 60: The Galapagos Penguins

While the Galapagos penguins live on and near the Galapagos Islands, their breeding grounds are ideal for laying eggs. These islands will keep their eggs nice and warm without the penguin having to do much work. The Galapagos penguin protects their eggs from the island's extreme heat by putting them into crevices in the ground, preferably between rocks.

That way, the eggs can be in the shade and stay warm due to the islands having temperatures of 69°F to 84°F. Male and female Galapagos penguins take incubation shifts in sitting on their eggs until they hatch. The incubation period of the Galapagos penguin is 42 days. And after that 45 days, the parent Galapagos penguins take care of their hatchling until they are 3-6 months of age when they become fully independent.

Lesson 61: The African Penguins

The African penguins live in Southern Africa, where temperatures are 41°F to 68°F. To me, these temperatures would be ideal for laying a clutch of eggs seeing as the African penguins are warm-blooded, and temperatures around 41 degrees Fahrenheit shouldn't bother them since they are most likely used to it.

African penguins put their eggs in holes they dug under bushes or boulders, and they even burrow the clutch of eggs in piles of guano. Incubation time for these eggs is 41 days, with both mom and dad penguin taking turns incubating the clutch of at least two eggs. The young hatchling is fully independent after 3-5 months of being hatched.

Chapter Review

This chapter is about the way different species of penguins keep their eggs.

Five things that I find interesting about how they keep their eggs are:

1) Penguins keep eggs on their feet

2) Penguins keep eggs in holes they have dug

3) Penguins keep eggs in piles of guano

4) Penguins use stones as a nest for their eggs

5) Male penguins of each species take care of the egg just like the female, except the Emperor and King penguins.

The male King and Emperor penguins keep the egg on their feet. And since the female penguins only have one egg per breeding season, she leaves for the duration of the incubation period. These are the only two species of penguins where the male penguin cares for the egg independently.

Chapter 7: Penguin Colonies

Penguins tend to live in groups of penguins, which are called colonies. Some colonies range over 200,000 penguins. They live in colonies for protection from predators. Colonies can be big or small, but with numbers in some penguin species decreasing, the number of penguins in some colonies is declining.

Lesson 62: The Gentoo Penguin

For their protection, Gentoo penguins live in colonies. Even though these colonies have around 1,000 pairs. In 2007 the Gentoo penguin was placed on the near-threatened list by the IUCN. While their numbers have grown in the Antarctic Peninsula due to the protection treaty in 1959, other islands have decreased in the number of Gentoo penguins in their previous homes.

The cause of the decrease in colony numbers is believed to be disruptive fisheries or water pollution. Gentoo penguins live in small colonies compared to other species of penguins. Even though they are near threatened, they still have breeding grounds where more Gentoo penguins get together.

Lesson 63: The King Penguins.

The King penguins like traveling in groups even when outside of their colonies. The size of the travel groups is usually around 5 to 20 penguins. When King penguins gather together into their colonies, they number in the thousands.

Their colonies can even number close to 200,000 pairs. King penguins are highly social penguins, and I can imagine living with 199,999 other penguin pairs that it's not an option to be anti-social.

Lesson 64: The Snares Penguins.

Snares penguins have colonies on several islands. These islands are called The Snares. The Snares Islands are a group of islands located around the southern coast of the South Island in New Zealand. The two main islands that the snares penguins inhabit have colonies ranging from 3 to 1,300 pairs.

The amount of snares penguin colonies being so low is that there are about 25,000 breeding pairs of snares penguins left living in the wild. The status of these penguins is venerable, meaning they can become extinct at any notice.

Chapter Review

This chapter is about how many numbers in each colony of penguins are there. One interesting fact in this chapter is that some penguins like the King penguin can have colonies ranging up to 200,000 pairs.

A second interesting fact is that the snares penguins have a low number of breeding pairs of at least 25,000 pairs. The third fact is that snares penguins have their own group of islands called the Snares Islands.

Fact number four is that the Gentoo penguins have colonies ranging around 1,000 breeding pairs. And the fifth and final fact that I find interesting is that Gentoo penguins' colonies are usually small because they are an endangered species of penguins.

Chapter 8: Nesting Patterns

Just as penguins have different breeding patterns, they also have different nesting patterns. The nesting pattern is sort of like how a penguin keeps their egg, only with more research and detail into each species pattern. It also involves the incubation period and what each parent penguin does during that time. The nesting period then continues as the young penguins' parents take care of them until they are fully independent.

Lesson 65: The Adélie Penguins

The Adélie penguins have a nesting pattern of the females laying two eggs into a hole that she and her partner made and surrounding it with stones. The male and female will take turns sitting on their clutch of eggs until they have hatched. Male Adélie penguins tend to be the first parent to sit on the clutch while the female penguins go fishing for at least two days.

When the female Adélie returns to her nest and her mate, they change shifts, and the male then goes fishing for at least two days. They repeat this cycle until their clutch hatches after 32-34 days of incubation. The female tends to lay her eggs around December.

After the eggs have hatched, the mother and father penguins feed the young penguin, and both will leave to fish for more food. The young penguins then join a group of other young penguins called a crèche. They form these groups, so they are protected from predators. They also form crèches so that they can keep warm in extreme weather conditions while their parents are gathering food for them.

Young Adélie penguins hunt and fend for themselves and are fully independent at about two months old. After the parent penguins have raised them and taught everything, they need to survive on their own. The chicks can leave the nest and be on their own in the wild.

Lesson 66: The Chinstrap Penguins

Chinstrap penguins have an incubation period of up to 37 days. The male and female penguins begin forming a nest during the breeding season to prepare for the clutch of eggs to arrive. The female Chinstrap then lays her eggs during December. The clutch usually has at least two eggs, but a clutch with more than two is more likely to have surviving offspring.

The male and female Chinstrap penguins take turns incubating their nest. The female penguin will leave to fish for six days, and once she returns, the males do the same. This cycle is repeated every six days for 37 days.

Once the eggs are hatched, the chicks stay with both parents for the first month of life. After that one month, both parents leave, causing the chicks to join a crèche to survive. The young Chinstrap penguins are fully independent by the age of around two months old; this is when they get their adult feathers and then swim in the ocean.

Lesson 67: The Gentoo Penguins

The incubation period for the Gentoo penguins is 35 days. Each parent is gone from the nest, taking turns in 24-hour shifts. The Gentoo begin making their nests using stones due to the limited resources available on their island. Even the stones are in limited supply even though they are in high demand.

Male Gentoo tends to gain favor with female Gentoo by bringing her the best possible stone that he can find. That is when they become mates if she likes the stone. The Gentoo chicks stay in the nest for an average of 30 days.

When the parents leave the nest to gather more food, the chicks join crèches with other young Gentoo penguins. As the chicks reach approximately two months old, they can fend for themselves and even join their parents on fishing trips. Female Gentoos reach breeding maturity at three years old while the males do not reach sexual maturity until four years of age.

Chapter Review

In this chapter, you learned how every penguin has a different nesting pattern. Even if they sound the same on paper, I'm sure watching them in person gives a whole different perspective. I have chosen five facts that interested me in this chapter.

Fact number one that I found interesting while learning more about penguins' nesting patterns is that the Gentoo penguins sexually mature at different ages. The second fact I found interesting is that most penguins use stones to build their nest even though stones are in limited supply.

The third fact is that most of the penguin species seem to have the same age of being fully independent around the age of two months old. That intrigues me because I could fathom having to fend for myself at just two months old. But since their lifespans can be cut short by predators, penguins have to mature fast.

The fourth fact that is intriguing is that almost every penguin species lay at least two eggs in a single breeding period, with King and Emperor penguins being the exception and only having a single egg each breeding cycle. The last and final fact of this chapter that interests me is that 16 out of 18 species of penguin take turns watching over their egg. The male and females switch places every few days to give each other time to swim, stretch, and eat. Male King and Emperor penguins do not get to take breaks while watching over the egg. It doesn't seem quite fair to me.

Chapter 9: Incubation of Penguin Eggs

The incubation period varies between breeds of penguins. Some can have the same amount of time to incubate. But these three penguins have varying times of their incubation cycle. Incubating is when a bird, or in this case, a penguin, has to keep their eggs warm in several ways. In this chapter, we will learn about the time and way these penguins incubate their eggs.

Lesson 68: The Little Blue/Fairy Penguins

Little Blue penguins incubate their eggs together, male and female. They take turns sitting on their nests while the other parent goes fishing. The incubation period of the nestling is approximately 35 days. After incubating for 35 days, the clutch of up to three eggs hatch. Whichever parent comes back from fishing, then regurgitate the fish to feed their newborn penguins. Their fishing trips tend to last up to 10 days per each parent.

They continue with the feeding pattern of switching parents for at least one month of the nestling's life. After the first month of life, each chick joins the crèche formed by all the young penguins whose parents leave after one month. And when a Fairy penguin becomes fully independent, they are typically between the ages of 57 and 78 days old.

However, after 38 days of life, the parents begin teaching the nestlings how to forge for themselves and only take care of the chick during the night. After teaching the chicks everything they need to know on how to survive without their parents, the chicks are free to leave if they are between 57 and 78 days.

Lesson 69: The Emperor Penguins

Emperor penguins have an incubation period of 65 to 75 days. The male penguins are the ones that take care of the egg for almost four whole months. Emperor penguins only have one egg at a time due to the fact they do not make nests. With living Antarctica, they can't make a viable nest because of the freezing temperatures.

So, having discussed that the Emperor penguins cannot make nests in the freezing winter temperatures, they have to carry the egg around to keep it warm. The father penguins have a brood pouch that helps keep the egg warm and protected. After almost four months, the female returns from her long fishing trip.

By the time the mother returns, the egg has already hatched and is waiting for food. The father penguin is also hungry after fasting for the whole duration of the incubation period. The mother penguin then feeds the baby penguin the fish she has gathered from her four-month fishing trip.

Lesson 70: The Yellow-eyed Penguin

The eggs of yellow-eyed penguins need to be incubated in their nest for at least 39 to 50 days. During the incubation period, the parents take turns having one day shifts. When one parent is out fishing, the opposite parent is sitting on the nest, keeping the clutch of eggs warm.

After the chick has hatched, the switching shifts cycle continues until the young penguin is at least 100 days old. During the 100 days of raising the chicks, the parents take turns teaching them anything and everything they can so that the chicks will fend for themselves in the wild.

The only time that both of the parents of the 16 out of 18 penguin species will not take care of their eggs together is if one of the parents, unfortunately, becomes prey while on their fishing trip. Other than that, almost every time, each penguin returns to their mate and chick.

Chapter Review

This chapter is about the incubation period of penguin eggs. I choose three penguin species that I thought would be more interesting to learn about with their incubation, seeing as they don't have much information about them online.

Fact number one is that most, well, almost every penguin species except two of them take turns incubating their egg(s). The second fact that I find interesting from this chapter is that the incubation period varies differently from each of the three penguins I choose to learn about using their cycle for incubating.

The third fact is that Fairy penguins take shifts in 10-day increments with no complaints. The female takes ten days to fish, and when she returns, her male partner takes ten days off to go fishing. From most of the educational websites I read, I assumed most penguins took on 1 to 3 days shifts at most, but not the Fairy penguins.

Out of the three penguins I choose for this chapter, the yellow-eyed penguins take the longest to become fully independent and live on their own without the help of their parents. That interesting fact (to me) is fact number four. And last but not least, fact number five, during the whole duration of the incubation period, the male Emperor penguins have to fast for almost four months by not taking turns hunting for fish while the female penguin is gone for four months until the egg has hatched.

Chapter 10: How Fast Can Penguins Swim?

Most penguins like to cruise while they fish. It makes it easier on the digestive system if they relax while swimming in the ocean. Each penguin breed swims at different rates per hour, but the miles per hour usually stay between 5 to 9 miles per hour. This way, they can spot their prey and enjoy being in the ocean at the same time. If they are in danger of becoming prey, they can swim a whole lot faster.

In this chapter, I will be answering a few questions with at least two questions per penguin. These questions are, do penguins plan on diving for their food? Will they dive and resurface like dolphins? Are they just spotting out where their food tends to stay? Or are they running from seals, sharks, or killer whales?

Lesson 71: The Gentoo Penguin

Swimming rates of the Gentoo penguin can vary based on several things.

Question one, do they plan on diving for their food? Just as humans do, penguins dive into the ocean to get deeper; only they are searching for food; most humans are not. Now, we need to figure out whether they swim slow or fast, so they can dive deeper.

Most of the time, when having to dive deeper into the ocean, you would put some force behind your strokes. Penguins will either do that same thing or plan on diving deep before getting into the water. They will jump into the water and begin going faster to get deeper.

So, let's say the Gentoo penguin likes cruising at a steady 4 miles per hour. To get deeper into the ocean while going faster, they will have to speed up to at least 7 or 8 miles per hour.

Now for the next question, will they dive and resurface like dolphins? Well, if you look online, you will find videos of penguins leaping out of the water's surface. Do they leap as high as dolphins? No, most likely not.

Gentoo penguins tend to leap out of the water for fun like dolphins. It's one of the ways they enjoy being in the ocean. This also helps them get back to their islands faster when they do not want to swim very fast.

Lesson 72: The Little Blue/Fairy Penguin

The Little Blue penguin is the slowest swimming penguin in the world. The fastest these penguins go is at least one mile per hour. So, the questions we will be discussing for the Fairy penguins will be, are they just spotting out where their food tends to stay? And the next question will be, do they plan on diving for their food?

I want to go over the question, are they running from seals, sharks, or killer whales? But since the fastest these penguins tend to swim is one mile per hour, I don't think they'll be doing much running from these predators because hopefully, they will not travel much farther than a couple of miles away from their shoreline.

The diet of a Fairy penguin consists of krill and small fish. The answer to 'are they just spotting out where their food tends to stay at' is that yes, they tend to cruise while spotting out their food. With their diet consisting of krill, they will need to keep a sharp eye out for them. Just as much as the small fish they eat, which is usually anchovies and sardines.

The next question is, do they plan on diving for their food? With their food being what it is, they most likely have to dive to get their food. Krill tends to hide from their predators, being at least 320 feet beneath the surface of the ocean. Anchovies tend to be near the ocean's surface and at least 60 miles away from any shoreline. Sardines stay in the column of water between offshore and nearshore along the coastal lines.

Lesson 73: The Emperor Penguin

Now the Emperor penguin is categorized as the largest penguin in the world. So, with that being said, they should be the fastest penguin, right? Wrong, the Emperor penguin is not the fastest just because they are the largest penguins. Gentoo penguins happen to be the fastest penguins in the world.

So, the two questions that we will answer using the Emperor penguin's information are, 'Will they dive and resurface like dolphins?' and 'Are they running from seals, sharks, and killer whales?'

Well, let's talk about question number two since we have not chosen that question for the other two penguins. Are they running from seals, sharks, and killer whales? Hmm, let's think about this for a second. With the Emperor penguin being the largest penguin, would seals be their predators? The surprising answer to that question is yes, leopard seals are predators to the Emperor penguins.

So, answering question two, 'are they running from seals, sharks, and killer whales?', yes, Emperor penguins tend to have to run from these three predators. However, it's mainly leopard seals and killer whales that want to eat Emperor penguins.

Going back to question one, 'will they dive and resurface like dolphins?' The simple answer is yes. Although they do not jump out of the water like dolphins, they tend to jump out of the water only when coming back onto land.

Chapter Review

One interesting fact I found about how fast penguins swim is that the Gentoo penguins are the fastest swimmers to reach speeds of up to 22 miles per hour. Fact number two that interests me and hopefully you, is that most penguins prefer to cruise at the minimum rate per hour to enjoy swimming and spot out their food.

The third fact is that krill live at least 320 below the water's surface, so the penguins who eat them as a big part of their diet have to dive pretty deep to get the food they need for the day. And during the incubation period, they most likely have to gather twice as much if not more food depending on how long of shifts each breeds male and female take.

Fact number four is the Little Blue penguin happens to be the slowest swimming penguin in the world despite being the smallest penguin. You would think that being the smallest penguin would make them faster because they aren't as heavy, right? However, being small doesn't always come with the perks one thinks it should.

The last and final fact from this chapter that I find interesting is that the Emperor penguins are not the fastest penguins either, but they use their size and strength to propel themselves out of the water and onto land like a torpedo. I'm sure this is a handy tool when fleeing from predators.

They build up their speed, and once they are fast enough, they dive and resurface quickly to propel themselves onto land a few feet away from the shoreline, giving them added protection from whatever is their predator at the time. This concludes my chapter review. I hope you enjoyed the fun facts I thought stuck out the most.

Chapter 11: There are 18 Species of Penguins

Lesson 74: Australia and New Zealand Have Six Species of Penguins

In Australia and New Zealand, there are six species of penguins. I thought there would be more penguin species living in Antarctica yet Australia and New Zealand have six, which is more than in Antarctica.

Each breed of penguin has its unique qualities and characteristics. The six penguin species in Australia and New Zealand are the Yellow-eyed penguin, Snares penguin, Royal penguin, Erect-crested penguin, Fiordland penguin, and the Little Blue/Fairy penguin.

Lesson 75: The Yellow-Eyed Penguins

The Yellow-Eyed Penguins are native to New Zealand. They are not migratory birds. The areas they tend to stay around are the southern areas of New Zealand. This penguin breed can live to be up to 20 years old.

The yellow-eyed penguin's feature and inherited trait and how they got their name is their yellow eyes, and the feathers surrounding their eyes are also yellow. Their feathers help to distinguish the young from the adult penguins.

Young yellow-eyed penguins do not get the yellow feathers around their eyes until their first molt at the age of one. The young penguins also have a grayer head, then black and yellow. They get darker with the yellow feathers during their first molting year, which happens in February and can take as long as four weeks.

The breeding patterns of yellow-eyed penguins are during the end of summer into the early spring of the next year. Meaning their breeding period is beginning in August and ends in March of the following year. Yellow-eyed penguins keep their eggs warm and protected by making scrapes in the ground filled with and surrounded by leaves, sticks, and grass.

Male and female yellow-eyed penguins take turns watching over their eggs just like almost every other penguin species. When the mother is watching over the nest, the father is out fishing and vice versa.

They continue doing this schedule until the incubation period is over, and eggs have hatched. The shifts of the mother and father change every day, and during the incubation period, each parent gets to eat and take a break while fishing. After the incubation of the eggs is complete and the chicks hatch, then the guarding period begins.

Each yellow-eyed penguin parent continues the shift schedule from the incubation period with one parent protecting the chicks while the other is off fishing. They guard and protect the chick or chicks if both eggs made it, from predators and other penguins who may become territorial over their nest and chicks if they feel threatened by any other chick.

Yellow-eyed penguins become fully independent around 100 days after they have hatched from the egg and been cared for by their parents. The parents teach the chicks what they need to know about living independently and show them how to catch their food. Once they are ready, they leave the nest to make their own lives.

Female yellow-eyed penguins may become sexually mature and ready to reproduce by the age of two or even three years old. While the males will not be sexually mature until they are at least three years of age, but they almost be late bloomers and not be ready to reproduce until they become five years old.

When the eggs are laid, they do not come out one after the other there is a span of three to five days in between the eggs. The incubation period begins after the second egg has been laid to hatch around the same time in November. Yellow-eyed penguins have also been known by the names hoiho or tarakaka by those living in the yellow-eyed penguins' territory of New Zealand.

It was once believed that the yellow-eyed penguins were related to the Eudyptula minor penguin or most commonly known as the Little Blue or Fairy penguin. With more in-depth molecular research, it has been shown that Yellow-eyed penguins belong in the genus of penguins called Eudyptes. This group of penguins is commonly referred to as the crested penguins. And like we have discovered, this penguin is a piscivorous bird, as are the rest of the penguin species.

Unlike other bird species and some penguin species, the Yellow-eyed penguin tends to remain quiet and may only make noises at their nesting and breeding grounds. The call they make is a shill-like, bray-like call. Something that I found interesting is that yellow-eyed penguins don't just eat sardines and anchovies. They also eat opal fish as well as red and blue cod. They are demersal species living near the ocean floor, making up 90 percent of the yellow-eyed penguins' diet.

While the yellow-eyed penguins are listed as an endangered species, they are also considered one of the rarest of all the penguin species. This may be due to their decreasing numbers, but the reason for them being considered rare is their eye color. Though these penguins have a population of only around 4,000 left, these penguins are also thought to be the most ancient of all the penguin species living today.

The U.S. Endangered Species Act granted protection to the yellow-eyed penguins in August the year of 2010. Simultaneously, the Department of Conservation and the Yellow-eyed Penguin Trust have established a reserve to protect at least more than 10 percent of the New Zealand mainland penguins. They established this in November of 2007 in the Catlins at Long Point. So, while these penguins are endangered and risk extinction, there have been preparations in place to slow and hopefully stop the decreasing numbers.

In North Otago and on the Otago Peninsula during the spring of 2004, 60 percent of Yellow-eyed penguin chicks died due to a previously undescribed disease. Corynebacterium is a bacterium of the genus that causes diphtheria. This is just the second part of the disease that killed off 60 percent of penguin chicks in the yellow-eyed penguins' hatching season. The first and primary infection that killed off these penguins is still unknown.

There are no exhibits in zoos for the yellow-eyed penguin because they won't reproduce in captivity even if they are mated. This could be a sign that yellow-eyed penguins find being trapped in enclosed spaces depressing. When penguins, or any animal for that matter, are depressed, they go into a state of self-destruction.

They may not eat, drink, or even interact in the same manner as they have before. With penguins, this feeling could be even more enhanced due to the fact their instincts tell them something is wrong and that they need wide open spaces to feel free, as well as other penguins, as they would have in a colony of penguins.

Lesson 76: The Snares Penguin

The snares penguin can have a lifespan of 15-20 years. When a snares penguin goes through molting, they tend to stay on land for 3-4 weeks, leaving them without food during this time. They can be aggressive and territorial, especially when challenged in their rank.

While in confrontations with other snares penguins to help define each penguin's rank, they push each other away with their beaks as they flap their wings. Snares penguins are diurnal breeders. The young molt during

January to March at the edges of their colonies on coastal rocks. They live on islands near New Zealand.

The islands that group the snares' territory is a range of 1.158 miles or 3 square kilometers. Snares penguins may look cute and cuddly, but they will respond in their aggressive manner if they feel threatened.

The snares penguins are a part of the genus called Eudyptes robustus. Snares penguins are yellow-crested small to medium-sized penguins being 19.5 to 27.5 inches tall and weighing around 5.5 to 8.8 pounds. The coloration of the snares penguins is a dark blue to black on their backs and faces while they have traditional white stomachs.

Its bill or beak, whichever you prefer, is a reddish-brown color. They also have a bright yellow bushy strip on their face looking like eyebrows. This part of the snares penguin coloration is called a crest, which is why they are part of the crest penguin genus and match molecular DNA.

The main areas near New Zealand that the snares penguin lives in are North East Island, Broughton Island, and Western Chain. They mainly enjoy krill's delicacy, but if they do not catch enough krill, they will eat squid and small fish.

The IUCN has declared these penguins in a state of vulnerability because they only use a small island to reproduce. As for the migration patterns of the snares penguin, very little is known except for these penguins' breeding season, which is during the New Zealand summer. Starting in September and finishing with the incubation and hatching of the new chicks by the end of January.

When nesting snares, penguins tend to choose densely wooded areas under the cover of trees in the Olearia forests. However, they may also nest along the coastal rocks of their breeding grounds. While making their nest, they gather twigs, grass, pebbles, peat, or leaves to cover the bottom of the swallow hole they have dug for the eggs.

During their nesting activities, the vegetation surrounding the nest sites tend to die out, so the snares penguins must move on to a new site in which to nest. Even though they all breed on one island, they make separate colonies, usually containing 10 to 1,200 nests being made. Those whose colonies nest near streams have the advantage of fresh and close water to bathe in and drink from.

Many of the colonies can be located pretty far from any stream, seeing as they do not find it essential to be right on the water's edge. Though these penguins are not currently on the endangered species list, they could very well be listed on there soon if not listed as extinct. Because these penguins are only nesting and breeding on one island, they risk becoming extinct due to new and very possible threats.

These threats include increasing water temperature driving away their food source due to global warming. Then there is overfishing that causes a decrease in the amount of food surrounding their islands. And a new predator being introduced to their islands could end up very bad for these penguins. Thankfully the government of New Zealand took swift action protecting the Snares Islands and its feeding grounds surrounding their habitats.

Male snares penguins leave the female snares during the incubation period waiting for the eggs hatch to go on a two-week-long fishing trip. This is the foraging pattern of the snares penguins during the incubation of the eggs. Once the males return from their trip, the females then take their leave, going on their fishing trip for usually less than seven days. Female snares return to the nest just in time to see their eggs hatch.

During the guarding stage the comes right after the chicks have hatched from their eggs, the mother is the sole provider of food, taking one to three-day fishing trips to gather enough food for the father penguin to leave for his usual two-week long trip. Baby penguins and the unhatched eggs can become prey to other seabirds like the skuas and petrels. This is the reason snares penguins have a guarding stage, though, in my opinion, the male penguins should be there longer to protect their young just as much as the females.

While building the nest for the clutch of eggs, which is usually two eggs, they have a higher chance of at least one chick surviving. The male penguins do most of the work, from digging the shallow hole to gathering twigs, pebbles, grass, peat, and leaves to lay in at the bottom of the nest. They also gather mud to add around the edges to make the nest just slightly above ground level. This acts as a barrier and place for the parents to sit on their eggs during incubation.

Like the yellow-eyed penguins, the female snares penguins her eggs three to five days apart and does not start the incubation period until she has laid her second egg. In the case of the snares penguin, the second egg to be laid is usually the biggest and is more likely to survive through the incubation period and hatch. Though it is not uncommon for the first egg to hatch along with the second, it may not thrive as well due to being smaller and less favorable than the bigger egg.

Both parents incubate the eggs, and for the beginning ten days of incubation, the switch swifts most likely daily. After the ten-day trial period, the male will take his two-week fishing trip. After he returns, the parents strengthen their bond by bowing to each other and using the trumpeting call. After hatching, the male snares penguin stays to guard the chick while he lets the female snares penguin go on a three-week foraging trip, though she returns every night to feed her chick.

Once the chick has molted for the first time, his or her parents stop providing food for the chick as they should be capable of fishing for themselves. With only 11 weeks after hatching, the snares penguin has become fully independent. This means they can live independently, forage for themselves, and protect themselves from their common predators, such as the sea lion, leopard seal, skuas, and petrels.

Lesson 77: The Royal Penguin

The royal penguins are the largest penguin of the crested penguins, measuring 26-30 inches tall and weighing about 6-18 pounds. They reach sexual maturity between the age of 7 to 9 years old. The Royal penguin lives in Australia and around the sub-islands of Antarctica.

After mating, they leave their breeding island returning to their home island due to being migratory penguins. Royal penguins are very social, and they prefer to live in large colonies. To increase their survival rate, royal penguins spend large amounts of time close to each other while on land to protect each other from land predators.

When searching for their mate or offspring, they must rely on their ability to recognize their voices. The interesting thing to me is that all penguins have a unique call for their young, mates, and everyone else and the fact that male royal penguins are bigger than the females.

The royal and macaroni penguins have been spotted to interbreed with each other. This happening between the two species is rare, though. Their breeding ground is the Macquarie Islands, and this is the only place royal penguins tend to breed.

During the breeding season, which is about one month long, with mating beginning in September and laying eggs starting in October, the incubation of the clutch is usually around 35 days long. The nest that holds the clutch of eggs is typically a scrape or hole in the ground surrounded by twigs, pebbles, grass, or leaves.

While incubating the eggs, each parent takes 12-day fishing trips. After the egg has hatched, the father will stay with the chick for its first two or three weeks of life. Meanwhile, the mother is out gathering food for both the chick and her mate. Each parent will then take daily turns of bringing the chick food at least three times a day for one month. Once the chick has reached two months of age, they are fully independent.

Upon becoming fully independent, the chicks molt their baby feathers and grow into their adult plumage, leaving the nest to fend for themselves. Juvenile and adult royal penguins feed mainly on krill but will also eat small squid and fish.

The IUCN has placed the royal penguins on the near-threatened list even as they are at risk of being endangered. From the 1870s to 1919, the Tasmanian government gave out hunting licenses for catching royal and king penguins. The hunters caught up to 150,000 royal and king penguins.

This was done during that period to harvest the oil from each penguin. Gathering half a liter from each penguin, the factory at Macquarie Island used 2,000 penguins at a time in 1905. The population of both king and royal penguins was at least 3 million penguins or more. Now there are around 850,000 mating pairs left after ending the processing of these poor penguins.

Lesson 78: The Erect-crested Penguin

These penguins can be found along the coasts of Australia and New Zealand, while their breeding areas are found near New Zealand. This marks the Erect-crested penguins as migratory birds. Erect-crested penguins are around 26 inches tall and weigh about 13 pounds on average.

During early September, male and female erect-crested penguins gather together in large colonies to breed along the rocky shores of their breeding grounds. Breeding couples usually lay two eggs during October, with only one egg surviving each time.

Ecologists noted that the number of erect-crested penguins has been decreasing since the late 1970s. In 1998 the population of breeding couples in the Bounty Islands fell from 115,000 in 1978 to 28,000. The breeding pairs population had dropped from 115,000 also in 1978 on the Antipodes Islands to 49,000-57,000 in 1995. Scientists have not been able to figure out the reason for their declining numbers.

The erect-crested penguin is in the genus called Eudyptes sclateri. Their breeding grounds are at the Bounty and Antipodes Islands only. These penguins are listed as endangered by the International Union for Conservation of Nature.

Due to the New Zealand Department of Conservation protecting these penguins, little information has been obtained about them. The most recent study of the erect-crested penguin is how mates are chosen. The biology and DNA are not known about due to not getting the needed samples to study the erect-crested penguin.

It has been noticed that their pre-molting season is between February and March. During this time, both male and female erect-crested penguins take longer foraging trips than usual. During their molting period, they cannot get in the water as they are not water-resistant.

They also take longer foraging trips during the months leading up to their breeding season in September. Erect-crested penguins take these long trips to gather and eat more food because they do not eat as much during molting and the incubation of their eggs, so they begin to lose about half of their body weight.

During the late 1970's it was estimated that the population of erect-crested penguins was at 230,000 breeding pairs of penguins on their breeding grounds of Bounty and Antipodes Islands. Though now that calculation has been questioned as to the accuracy of this estimate.

Now the population of erect-crested penguins is believed to be 150,000 individual sexually mature erect-crested penguins left. They have been put on the endangered species list by the IUCN's Red List and have been granted protection by the U.S. Endangered Species Act.

Lesson 79: The Fiordland Penguin

Fiordland penguins make their egg nest between tree roots, under bushes, or in holes without using many nest-building materials. Their typical lifespan is 10-20 years. They weigh in at 6 to 7 pounds and are about 2 feet tall. These penguins end up growing barnacles on their tails because most penguins spend 75% of their lives in the sea. This sounds insane because I always thought barnacles could only form on the bottoms of boats and ships. Fiordland penguins can be found near Stewart and Solander Islands. They are monomorphic, meaning the male and female penguins look alike, as are most penguin species.

Most penguin species are like this, with the male and female looking very similar. Meanwhile, during July, the mating couples produce two pale-green eggs. Male Fiordland penguins guard and care for the hatchlings for the first few weeks of life while the female gathers food. The Fiordland penguins like to nest near tree roots and rocky ground in the coastal defense forest they need near.

Their breeding grounds include the West Coast of the South Island south of Bruce Bay and the Open Bay Islands. And also, around the outlying islands of the Stewart Islands and Rakiura. Though Fiordland penguins are native to New Zealand, there have been fossils found of them on the northernmost end of the South Island by Bruce Bay and at the North Island.

These penguins are in the genus known as Eudyptes pachyrhynchus. In the Eastern Polynesian language called Māori, Fiordland penguins have been known as tawaki and pokotiwha. They are part of the crested penguin family. The word 'pachyrhynchus' has been derived from the Ancient Greek translation of "thick" (pachy) "beak" (rhynchos).

A zoologist named George Robert Gray first discovered and described the tawaki in 1845 he was an English zoologist. The coloration of both male and female Fiordland penguins are dark blue-gray backs with white stomachs and the same yellow crest on their heads, where eyebrows would be, just as all crested penguins have.

They may have even been confused with the snares and erect-crested penguins, but upon closer inspection, you will see they do not have bare skin showing around their bills at the base where you would see nostrils. However, just like almost every penguin, the tawaki lay a clutch of eggs containing at least two eggs.

The first egg, as usual with penguins, is the relatively smaller one of the two. Incubation is at least 36 days long, with chicks hatching during September. The eggs are taken care of by both parents until they have hatched. The father watches over the chick for the first three weeks after hatching while the mother brings the food. And speaking of food, the Fiordland penguin diet has been reported as 85% cephalopods, mainly being Arrowhead squid. They also eat krill, red cod, and hoki, but they prefer squid.

In 2013 the Department of Conservation changed these penguins' status from vulnerable to becoming extinct to endangered. Causes for their decline numbers are the introduction of new predators such as dogs, rats, cats, and stoats. They also get scared due to humans' disturbance, resulting in the adult penguins' running away from the nests leaving their eggs and chicks.

Lesson 80: The Little Blue/Fairy Penguin

Now the fairy penguin is one of the penguins I am most excited to learn and teach about. I had no clue such a penguin existed. A blue penguin? That, to me, is amazing. So, all the information I learned about these penguins was very new to me, and I hope it'll be new and entertaining to you as well.

These penguins are often called the fairy penguin due to their small stature. In New Zealand, they go by the little blue penguin on account of their coloration, while they go by the fairy penguin in Australia due to their small size. These penguins often measure up to be 17 inches, but the smallest ones measure up to be 13 inches tall. The average weight of the fairy penguin is 3.3 pounds.

They can fend for themselves just after two months of being hatched. A fairy penguin can live up to 6.5 years in the wild and 25 years in captivity. Predators of this penguin are not common for most other penguins, and these predators are dogs, foxes, cats, reptiles, raccoons, and stoats. They are diurnal and like to spend most of their day in the ocean.

The little blue penguin was first described by Johann Reinhold Foster, a German naturalist, in 1781. There appear to be several subspecies of this penguin. And with genetic testing and analysis, it has been found that the Australian and Otago fairy penguins are distant relatives.

In 2011 the estimated population of the fairy penguins was around 350,000 to 600,000. And with the fact that new colonies have been discovered, there may be more or less now that haven't been counted. The areas in which fairy penguin colonies can be found are Australia, New Zealand, Jervis Bay Territory, Victoria, Tasmania, New South Wales, Western Australia, and South Australia.

The little penguins' diet is clupeoid fish, crustaceans, and cephalopods. In the year 2000, Port Phillip Bay's fairy penguin population was mainly barracouta, Arrowhead squid, and anchovy. While penguins in New Zealand prey on arrow squid, ahuru, Graham's gudgeon, slender sprat, and red cod. The not so common prey may include crab larvae, seahorses, eels, and jellyfish.

During the breeding season, male fairy penguins compete for mates by renovating or digging new burrows to show off to the females. After finding their mates and breeding together, the female lays her eggs in the burrow, either built by her mate or in caves and crevices they find.

So, for now, let's talk about when the chicks become fully independent. It takes around 7 to 8 weeks for the penguin chicks to go through their fledging period. This is just a fancy way of saying that the chicks have molted their juvenile feathers and gone into their first sets of adult feathers.

On Granite island, the penguin population has severely declined in numbers, with 2,000 fairy penguins in 2001 to 22 penguins being counted in 2015. This is due to a timber causeway between Granite island and the mainland. Usually, colonies of fairy penguins love in areas without dogs, foxes, and cats, but occasionally pathways between predators and penguins form, causing a decrease in population.

Fairy penguins have native land predators such as Rosenberg's goanna, tiger snake, and blue-tongued lizards. The chicks are prey for Rosenberg's goanna and the tiger snake while the blue-tongued lizard goes after the eggs. The sea animal that goes after the little blue penguin is the long-nosed fur seals. Research has shown that at least 40 percent of the long-nosed fur seals dropping contained little blue penguins remains.

Other predators to go after the fairy penguins are sharks (which is not often), barracouta Australian sea lions, and the white-bellied sea eagles. And out of all of these predators, one is also on the endangered species list. This animal just so happens to be the white-bellied sea eagle.

There were two mass deaths among the fairy penguin species, with the first mass death occurring in March doing the year 1935 in Port Phillip Bay. Molting and fatigue are followed by death, which is noticed during the early mass death of fairy penguins.

The second mass death happened in the Phillip Islands in Victoria. The month was not specified, but the event occurred in 1940. During this time, the fairy penguin population was thought to be at least 2,000 penguins. However, after the mass death happened, that population dropped to around 200.

Though the second mass death does not explain what happened exactly to these penguins. The condition they were in looked as if they were healthy. Clearly, though, that want the case song as almost all of them from Phillip Island died. So, it is believed a pathogen (infection) or disease took the lives of the fairy penguins during that year.

The relationship between the little blue penguins and humans have not always been kind. During the centuries, 19 and 20 fairy penguins were shot for the "sport" of it. People also captured these penguins just for their enjoyment of watching them. Who knows what else they did to these poor penguins just for their amusement?

Shipwrecked sailors would trap and eat them so they could survive. This is the same thing castaways did to the fairy penguins. Tanner's would also use their skins to make items out of little blue penguin skins. Their eggs were also gathered just as chicken eggs are gathered and used nowadays.

Tourism changed the way people see most penguins. There are even zoos that allow people to get up close and personal with penguins. I do not doubt that with people utilizing the resources they have, they will learn more about penguins and what can be done to help slow down or even stop the extinction of any penguin breed.

All penguins have multiple threats to their lives, especially being the little blue penguin. Due to the size and stature of the little blue penguin, they have many predators after them. Maybe even a bit more than other penguins that are not as small. For instance, they can be hunted by cats and even lizards and snakes.

The tiger snake that hunts the chick fairy penguins can get up to 2.5 meters long, which converted into feet is 8.2 feet long. And the blue-tongue lizards can be up to 24 inches long. Even the blue-tongue lizard does not get that big but still goes after the chicks in which they may be bigger than.

Fairy penguins may not be endangered as if now, but most populations on their territories are threatened. One of them is even at the risk of becoming endangered; even though the fairy penguins are being protected from various jurisdictions, they are still at risk for things that are even out of human control, sometimes, such as oil spills.

Lesson 81: Antarctica Has Five Species of Penguins

Antarctica is the coldest place globally, which would explain the myth behind all penguins loving the cold. But as you can see, there are only five species out of 18 that live in Antarctica. There are five species of penguins living in Antarctica. These five species are Emperor Penguins, King Penguins, Adélie Penguins, Gentoo Penguins, and Chinstrap Penguins.

Lesson 82: The Emperor Penguin

The Emperor penguin is the largest penguin measuring in at 43-51 inches tall and weighing 49-99 pounds. Their coloration is a black back and white belly with a pale-yellow breast and bright-yellow patches at their ear, making them sort of stick out in the snow and ice, but since they don't have land predators, it doesn't cause them to be in harm's way. They can survive cold temperatures as low as -76°F and blizzard winds of up to 124 miles per hour.

During those cold times, the emperor penguins form a group and circle together, which keeps them warm and protected. The inner penguins switch out with the penguin at the edge of the circle, and they repeat this cycle until warmer temperatures come.

Colonies of the emperor penguin can be as little as a few hundred or as big as over 20,000 pairs or 40,000 penguins. Their molting period starts in January and ends in February. Meaning their molting season is faster than other birds having 34 days to molt.

After doing my research, I realized I knew less about the emperor penguin than I thought. I hope that if you thought you knew everything about them and then found out something new about them, it was interesting and educational.

The emperor penguin may be the largest penguin alive, but that does not mean that they are immune to extinction threats. As of 2012 and being listed by the IUCN, they have been moved from the list of least concern to the near-threatening list.

Within the emperor penguin being on their near-threatened list, the numbers in their colonies have been counted to range in the thousands, at least near 5,000 mating pairs but can also range up to at least 10,000 mating pairs in one colony. As of the year 2012, scientists have counted around 595,000 emperor penguins remaining in the wild.

This estimated number of emperor penguins is larger than the last time their numbers were estimated in 1992 when their numbers ranged between 270,000 to 350,000 penguins. And as they are only found in Antarctica, scientists would have to travel from where they are from to tag and count all emperor penguins to have the exact number left today.

Emperors are one of the only two penguins that do not make a nest to incubate their eggs. Seeing as the females only lay one egg per year, they generally have large eggs. After the female lays the egg, she passes it on to the father, so there is no need to make a nest as the male penguin carries the egg by himself.

Fish is the main part of their diet. They eat the Antarctic silverfish the most. Emperors also include squid and krill into their regular diet. The glacial and the hooked squid are the main two squids they eat. Also, the Antarctic krill, the krill they eat the most of from the krill family.

Zoos had to use trial and error while figuring out how to raise an emperor penguin in captivity. In the 1960s, the first zoo to successfully raise the emperor penguin in captivity was the Aalborg Zoo, located in Denmark. One of the emperor penguins in the zoo lived to be around 20 years old in the zoo.

For them to have been successful, they had to use the trial and error method. During the use of this method, they discovered that emperor penguins need an arctic habitat to survive. The Aalborg Zoo built a chilled, possibly icy looking habitat to match the climate they are naturally made for.

In June, during the year 2011, an emperor penguin in Peka Peka near Wellington, New Zealand, was located on the beach dying. This poor penguin was dying because he had eaten 6.6 pounds of sand, most likely mistaking it for snow. He also had ingested stones and sticks, so he had to go through surgery to remove the sticks, sand, and stones from his stomach.

It took three months of surgery for the juvenile male emperor penguin, given the name 'Happy Feet.' The date of his full recovery was the 4th of September in 2011. The scientist who had saved this penguin placed a tracking device on him as they released him north of Campbell Island back in the Southern Ocean. Unfortunately, just after eight short days of tracking Happy Feet, they no longer received the tracking connection from his tracker, assuming it had slipped off and gotten lost rather than believe a predator may have eaten him.

Lesson 83: The King Penguin

King penguins are the second-largest penguin weighing in at an average of 33 pounds and having an average height of 37.2 inches. They closely resemble the Emperor penguins having the same yellow pattern on their breast and ear patches.

Only the yellow markings are dark yellow to orange on their breast and ear patches. They also have dark grey and black feathers along their backs. King penguins tend to live in the Sub-Antarctic Islands, where it just so happens to be characterized by beaches and valleys with no snow or ice.

They tend to breed on the same island that almost half the other penguin species live out in the wild. The king penguin is in the genus called Aptenodytes patagonicus; this means they are a part of two species of penguins commonly known as "the great penguins," including the emperor penguins.

A cool thing to learn about the king penguins is that they mainly eat lantern fish, krill, and squid. Lantern fish being small mesopelagic fish, they also use bioluminescence. King penguins have been recorded to dive far into the ocean of at least 1,000 feet or more.

During the breeding season, king penguins have several islands to go to, including sub-Antarctic islands that are in the northern regions of Antarctica, South Georgia (and no, as cool as it would be, this is not near the United States of America), and any other islands around Antarctica that are temperate.

King penguins have been recorded diving up to 771 feet into the ocean dating back to 1982. But the most recent record is of them diving at least 1,000 feet or more down into the ocean. They spend around five minutes underwater during their dives. King penguins take daytime trips and nighttime foraging trips, though, during the night, they will not dive as deep as to protect themselves from their predators who may be waiting for them.

Their diets consist of small fish, which mainly involve lanternfish, squid, and krill. Just a couple of squid types the king penguins enjoy are the hooked squid and the sevenstar flying squid. They also enjoy the young Gonatus antarcticus, which, if you look it up, this squid is kind of scary looking. The young Onychoteuthis is also another squid enjoyed by the king penguin.

And if I do say so myself, I would not come within 5 feet of either one of these scary looking squids. These king penguins are brave in my eyes. Who knows what they can do when they get older?

The king penguin does have quite a few predators to worry about. While it is believed or assumed by most people that the predators of penguins are mainly in the ocean, these few predators may show that predators can be anywhere.

Snowy sheathbill is a bird that, to me, looks quite like a seagull. With that being said, they are known as predators for king penguins. They are the only bird known to be native to the Antarctic region. The kelp gull is another southern hemisphere bird that, to me, looks like a seagull. However, they are usually found in Australia, South America, and New Zealand, where they are also considered predators to the king penguin.

King penguins are also hunted by Orcas, as are most penguins. However, I like to think that orcas and sharks tend to only go for the bigger penguins seeing them as having more meat and more filling. The leopard and Antarctic fur seals are also predators for king penguins though they have different attack styles against penguins.

Now moving on from talking about the list of predators the king penguin has, let's talk about these penguins' reproductive age. Both male and female king penguins are genetically able to breed by the time they are three years of age. Though they can breed by three years old, most king penguins wait until they are at least 5 to 6 years of age before mating.

And just like the emperor penguins, king penguins only lay one egg during each breeding season because the male penguin has to carry the egg on their feet. Now since I go into further detail about how king penguins keep their eggs, let us move to the next topic I'd like to talk about, and that's their conservation status.

So due to climate change, better known as global warming, is expected to cause a 70 percent decrease in the population of king penguins within at least the next 80 years. This may have more to do with their food source than any melting polar ice caps. As king penguins like a more temperate landscape, they do not live near icy or snowy areas.

They may have a significant decrease in the food supply because of the commercial fishing humans do. During the beginning period of the 1990s, at least 200,000 tons of the fish the king penguins also eat from called the myctophid fish, were gathered by humans to put in various stores for human consumption.

The IUCN standing for the International Union of Conservation of Nature declared the king penguin on the least concerned list. Back in 2004, the population size of king penguins grew, as did the breeding rates. With that being said, the leading causes as to why scientists believe that the king penguin population will drop drastically by 70 percent within the next 80 years are climate change and humans threatening their way to provide for not only themselves but also their family.

I found an adorable story on the internet of a male king penguin named Lala. He had gotten caught in the net of a fisherman in Japan. The family of the fisherman and himself took care of Lala until he was better. They then decided to keep him as their pet, most likely because he couldn't or wouldn't be able to survive in the ocean on his own anymore.

The TV show Animal Planet caught wind of this penguin and did a feature on him. After doing the feature about Lala, he became a viral video internet star. During the episode on Animal Planet, Lala can be seen waddling into a market near his home in Japan. Along with him, he brought his specialty made backpack for carrying his fish food home with him.

Lesson 84: The Adélie Penguin

The Adélie penguin was named in 1840 by an explorer named Jules Dumont D'Urville after his wife, Adélie. They have a migration pattern of 8,100 miles a year. So, they travel a decent amount. Could you travel more miles a year?

They average a height of 27.5 inches and a weight of 8.5-12 pounds. The coloration of these penguins is their identifying qualities. Their backs are black with blue-tipped feathers. They have white rings around their eyes, and their tail is longer than most other penguin species.

The beaks of the adélie penguins are red with a black tip. These penguins, for sure, look as if they are wearing a tuxedo. Adélie penguins are known for their more mellow nature. They tend to be highly social birds. Their colonies get along well with each other inside the colony more often than not. But I bet if one penguin tried to take another penguins' mate, they wouldn't be so mellow.

The adélie penguin is in the genus called Pygoscelis adeliae. They are one of three breeds of penguins from this genus. During the research, it is believed that the adélie penguins broke away from the other species of Pygoscelis almost 19 million years ago now. They also have impressive swimming skills for not being a very big penguin with speeds up to five miles per hour.

There is a very distinct mark that the adélie penguins have, which is one white ring around each eye. The adélie penguin's diet includes sea krill, ice krill, glacial squid, Antarctic krill, and the Antarctic silverfish.

Two of the food options they have include two jellyfish breeds, the Cyanea and Chrysaora. It was once believed that adélie penguins accidentally ate these jellyfish, but due to more research, it has been proven they seek these jellyfish out as a source of their diet.

Like most penguins, leopard seals are a predator for the adult adélie penguins while the eggs and nestlings are hunted by the south polar skuas and the giant petrels. Both of the seagull looking birds called the kelp gulls, and snowy sheathbills prey on the nestlings and eggs left unattended. Almost every penguin has the same predator due to being around the same general area.

During the 1980's adélie penguins declined in numbers along the Antarctic Peninsula while a series of increases in East Antarctica has counteracted the declining numbers. In March 2018, a 1.5 million adélie penguin colony was found. At one point, there had been 3.79 million mating pairs in around 251 colonies in the Antarctic region.

The adélie penguins are known to breed from October through February of the following year. They breed along the Antarctic shores, building nests to lay their eggs. These penguins use stones to build their nests even though there may not be enough stones for every penguin. A clutch of two eggs is laid by the females and taken care of by both parents.

The incubation period for adélie eggs is at a maximum of 34 days. Male and female take shifts, usually lasting 12 apiece. After hatching, the nestlings are then guarded and taken care of for the first 22 days of their life. At the end of those 22 days, they join groups of other young penguins called a crèche.

Even while joining a crèche, the nestlings' parents will still come back every night to feed their babies. They get their juvenile plumage or coat of feathers around 60 days of life, and they can venture out to sea on their own. Once the nestlings can leave their parents, they do not return to the breeding colonies until they have reached sexual maturity around three to five years of age.

The adélie penguins are listed on the near-threatened list by the IUCN. If their colonies went from 3.79 million breeding pairs to 1.5 million left, I could see why they are considered threatened. The change of their climate has to do with the majority of the concern on decreasing adélie penguin numbers. With sea ice changing and increased snowfall, these are a few of the climate changes that are affecting the adélie penguins.

Lesson 85: The Gentoo Penguin

Gentoo penguins are recognized relatively easily by the while strip that extends across their head like a bonnet. They also have a bright orange-red bill. They are the third-largest penguins reaching a height of 20-35 inches and weighing 9.9-19 pounds. The breeding grounds of Gentoo penguins tend to be free from ice, which sounds perfect for raising babies in. (Especially when they walk as soon as they hatch.)

These penguins are monogamous breeders; however, if any penguin causes infidelity within the colony, they are usually punished by being banished. Male Gentoo Penguins can earn favor with female penguins by giving her a choice of the best rock for her nest (kind of sounds like the same thing people do), where she will keep her eggs. Gentoo's diet mainly consists of crustaceans such as krill, with only 15 percent of their diet involving fish. These penguins also dive 450 times a day to fish for their food.

The genus name for the gentoo penguin is Pygoscelis papua. As you can see, they are the second of the three types of Pygoscelis penguin species making these penguins most closely related to the adélie penguins. The term Gentoo was used by the Anglo-Indian to separate Hindus from Muslims. The English use of the word possibly came from the Portuguese word gentio, meaning "pagan" or "gentile."

Gentoo penguins have also been known as the "Johnny penguin" because the Spanish name Juanito sounds similar to Gentoo, and it also means Johnny in English. The gentoo penguin gene separated from the other Pygoscelis penguins roughly around 14 million years ago. Now there are two subspecies of the genus Pygoscelis papua, and they are Pygoscelis papua ellsworthi and Pygoscelis papua papua.

The genus Pygoscelis came from the term, "rump-tailed" and the gentoo penguins are stereotypical penguins for this name as their tail sticks out from off their bottom and sweeps back and forth as they waddle everywhere they walk. A stand out characteristic that I noticed right off the bat is they have a fairly bright red-orange and black bill.

Breeding areas tend to be on sub-Antarctic islands. One of the main breeding colonies happens to be located in the Falkland Islands. Gentoo penguins can breed monogamously due to the population of breeding penguins is over 600,000 penguins. After breeding, the females lay two eggs being the same weight of 4.6 ounces.

With most gentoo penguins living around the Antarctic Peninsula, their diet consists mainly of krill. Though if they get the opportunity to eat more fish and squid, they have been known for going for them, seeing as most of the time, fish only makes up 15 percent of their diet.

Having populations of gentoo penguins in Bird Island and South Georgia rapidly declining, some people believe this is putting a damper on the overall species number. And because these are not the only areas to experience population decreases in the gentoo penguin species. Even with this fact, IUCN in 2019 listed the gentoo penguins as least concerned for extinction.

A quick cool fact is that the operating system known as Gentoo Linux is named after the Gentoo penguin. The cool fact about this is that they named the operating system after this penguin seeing as the gentoo penguins swim the fastest among the other penguin species. And Gentoo Linux strives to be high performance in the way their system operates.

Lesson 86: The Chinstrap Penguin

The Chinstrap penguin has many names including, Bearded penguin, Stonecracker penguin because of their harsh and loud call, and Ringed penguin. It got its name due to the thin black strap under its head/chin making it look like wearing a helmet. (I'm sure they do need to protect their heads; they dive into icy cold water daily.)

They weigh in at 7.1-11.7 pounds, measuring in the height of 27-30 inches, with the males tending to be larger than the females. Their diet is krill, shrimp, squid, and fish. The Chinstrap penguin is considered to be the most ill-mannered and aggressive of the penguin species.

One interesting story I found about the Chinstrap penguin is that in the Central Park Zoo in New York City, two male penguins formed a "pair" bond. Their names are Roy and Silo. They took turns trying to hatch a rock until the zookeeper replaced it with a fertilized Chinstrap penguin egg. Chinstrap penguins, just like all penguins, feel more natural and free when hatching an egg.

The scientific name for the chinstrap penguin is Pygoscelis antarcticus. They were originally given the name Aptenodytes antarctica by a man named Johann Reinhold Forster back in 1781. This name for the chinstrap penguins grouped them into the same genus as two other penguins called the emperor and king penguins.

However, in 1990 the chinstrap penguins were removed from the genus of Aptenodytes antarctica and placed in the genus of Pygoscelis antarcticus, matching them with the Gentoo and Adélie penguins listing them as closely related.

Chinstrap penguins eat the same thing as almost every penguin does, which are small fish, shrimp, squid, and krill. With a thick layer of blubber with the addition of their waterproof feathers, chinstrap penguins are kept warm while swimming in the freezing waters of the Antarctic. They also have the same predators due to living in the same region.

The incubation period for the chinstrap eggs to hatch is at least 37 days after being laid. Chinstrap penguins are considered the most ill-tempered penguin breed, and this is a perfect quality when protecting their eggs and newly hatched chicks.

The chinstrap penguin's conservation status is listed as least concern because their population number is estimated to be around 8 million penguins. However, scientists believe that the number is decreasing because of climate change, which is a problem for all penguin species.

Lesson 87: Near South America, There are Three species of Penguins

Islands and territories near South America have three species of penguins, which are, Magellanic penguins, Humboldt penguins, Galapagos penguins. These penguins have been classified to be nearest relatives.

They tend to live near or past South America and usually don't venture into the Northern Hemisphere, but one of these penguins live close enough to it to be considered to live in the Northern Hemisphere. Just which penguin is it, you ask; well, we will have to find out together.

Lesson 88: The Magellanic Penguins

These penguins were named in 1520 after being spotted by a Portuguese explorer named Fernando de Magellan. The males are typically larger than the females, but both parents' weights drop as they raise their young. The height of these penguins is 24-30 inches tall, and their weight is 6-14.3 pounds. The diet of a Magellanic penguin is cuttlefish, squid, fish, sardines, and anchovies.

These penguins tend to gather in nesting colonies in the Falkland Islands and the coasts of southern Chile and Argentina during the breeding season. Breeding season begins in September and ends in February or

March when the hatchlings can leave the nesting colonies.

Magellanic penguins like to lay their eggs in places where the temperatures stay around or over 68°F, which sounds like a very nice place to live, so why would they leave? The male and female often take turns incubating the eggs so the other can forage for food. They lay two eggs, with the first egg being more likely to survive.

Magellanic penguins are monogamous and mate with the same partner every year. Males arrive at the nesting grounds first to reclaim their previously nesting spot. They can find their mate just by the call of their voice alone.

Just one threat to these penguins is oil spills. Oil spills alone kill 20,000 adults and 22,000 young penguins each year around the coasts of Argentina. Another threat to these penguins, mainly the young penguins, is tourist exposure. The hatchlings show signs of stress while encountering tourists.

This can cause elevated corticosterone levels in their blood, which leads to interrupted development of the muscle strength immune and growth function. In the wild, the Magellanic penguin tends to live 25 years, but if they were to live in captivity, they could survive for up to 30 years.

The fact that I find unique is the young penguins usually have blotched patterns on their feet but fade as they enter adulthood, and after the age of ten, their webbed feet are usually now black. I always thought that penguins had orange or yellow feet. I never knew they could have black feet.

The Magellanic penguin genus name is Spheniscus magellanicus. They are listed as near threatened. An estimated breeding number of Magellanic penguins is around 1.5 million. Magellanic penguins migrate from Chile, Patagonia, the Falkland Islands, Argentina, and even go to Brazil.

Closest relatives to the Magellanic penguins are the Galapagos, African, and Humboldt penguins. And surprisingly enough, they all look very similar to each other. With the Magellanic penguins living near the Atlantic Ocean coast of South America, they do not have to experience any food shortage like their relative, the Galapagos penguins.

The diet of the Magellanic penguin includes cuttlefish, krill, squid, and other types of crustaceans. Just like other penguins, they all end up swallowing saltwater. Luckily penguins have a gland around their nose that excretes the salt from their bodies, so they do not dry out and become sick.

During the breeding season, these penguins migrate in flocks to hunt for food on their way to their nesting grounds. Once they reach their chosen nesting place, there are at least 20 nests for the eggs every 1,076.3 square feet. Magellanic penguins build their nest near the roots of bushes or inside of burrows they made or found.

The females end up laying two eggs while sharing incubation shifts with the father penguin for the maximum incubation period of 42 days. The shifts last for at least 10-15 days. After the penguin chicks hatch, they are then cared for and guarded by their parents for a maximum of 29 days, being fed every two or three days.

Every Magellanic penguin mates with the same partner for years unless, of course, they are unable to conceive eggs together. Females can find their previous mates just by the males calling for them. After breeding season is over, they all return to their home colonies for the winters.

The conservation status of the Magellanic penguin is near threatened even though they have millions of penguins. Millions of penguins live among Chile and Argentina coasts. So with their status being near threatened even at millions of them, they are declining in numbers.

Magellanic penguins face many of the same predators that other species of penguin face. Then, Magellanic penguins and many penguins face three additional main threats: oil spills, mass deaths, and climate change. Climate change is a big one that every penguin has to deal with. They may even become extinct due to the changing of our climate, which is also their habitat.

Oil spills cause a lot of damage to marine life, which includes penguins. When covered in oil, it is tough for them to swim while being covered in a thick gooey substance. Not being able to swim is not the only bad thing to happen when there is an oil spill. They could end up ingesting oil into their stomach and lungs, which will inevitably kill them.

Mass deaths occur when diseases and infections spread between the colony at rapid speeds. These can include any spreadable diseases and infections like diphtheria. Though in 2010, at least 550 Magellanic penguins were located along the coastline of Brazil, researchers believe their cause of death was starvation. Back before 2010, there were only ten penguins expected to be found dead along the shores within a year's time span.

Meanwhile, in a little further ahead in time to the year 2012, during June, most likely along the same shores of Brazil, a recorded number of at least 742 Magellanic penguins were found washed up on shore in what was considered a decomposed state. The cause of death was ruled as "natural cause" after being investigated even though these numbers of dead penguins included young ones.

Lesson 89: The Humboldt Penguins

The Humboldt penguin is named after an explorer named Alexander von Humboldt. The cold-water current they swim in is also named after this explorer. They are a migrating species of penguin. They prefer to nest in burrows of guano, caverns surrounded by vegetation, and rocky coasts. These penguins are found only on the Pacific coastline of South America. They have also been seen using real dirt to dig holes into the ground on a few Peruvian Islands.

They are medium-sized penguins measuring in at 22-28 inches tall and weighing 8-13 pounds. Diet consists primarily of pelagic schooling fish. They can gather more fish during overnight trips because the Humboldt penguin likes to leave their island after sunrise to gather fish. These penguins tend to catch the fish from below using short, shallow dives. Humboldt penguins have different calls that they use.

The Yell is a warning if anyone gets too close to them if ignored, it is followed by chasing and being pecked at. The bigger the colonies, the more aggressive and territorial these penguins become. The Peep is called out by chicks who are hungry. The Bray and Courtship Bray are similar because they can be used in calling for a mate, but the posture is different. During the Courtship Bray, the penguins stand facing one another with their necks and heads pointed up with their flippers out to the side.

The Bray posture is the penguin pointing their head up and slowly flapping their flippers. The Throb is a soft call used between pairs at their nest. The Haw is a short cry given by young penguins alone in the water and paired penguins when one is in the water and the other is inland. Most penguins molt during mid-January and mid-February. Humboldt penguins become hyperphagic during their pre-molting period. Their feathers are molted and replaced during two weeks.

Like every other penguin we have talked about thus far, the Humboldt penguin has a scientific name that they can go by, the genus called Spheniscus humboldti. They are a migrant breed of penguin. The reason I say this is because not all penguins migrate.

Some chose not to migrate as they do not need to follow their food source.

These penguins tend to choose the coastal areas of Chile and Peru to make their colonies and have their habitat for when they return from breeding. So, speaking of breeding, Humboldt penguins use nests for their clutch of eggs, but the materials they use may surprise people.

While they choose to nest along the island's rocky coast, they choose nesting materials that are not always easy to find. One of the few things they use to make the nest that will hold their eggs is guano. Humboldt penguins will likely dig a big enough hole into probably a dry pile of guano. They also use scrapes in the ground, which are essentially holes in the ground. They either were made by the penguin using it, made by another penguin previously, or just by finding a crack in the ground.

Usually, when making their own nest, if the males are the ones to make the nest themselves before the females arrive, they will try to make it look the best possible to impress the females. If their mate from the previous year returns, they will sit at the nest and call for them until they are found.

One cute fact I just found out about the Humboldt penguin is that in Peru, they are called 'pajaro-niño,' which in English means 'baby-bird' due to the way they walk. They waddle with their wings swaying along with them, causing them to look like toddlers walking along the beaches.

These penguins feed predominantly on pelagic fish that gather in schools. Humboldt penguins need daylight to fish as they are visual hunters. And because they need light to fish, their foraging patterns differ slightly based on the amount of light penetration in the water where they live.

One foraging pattern happens when penguins fail to breed. They take longer fishing trips while staying at the breeding grounds. They also do not need to take as many fishing trips as those who have successfully bred.

Threats to the Humboldt penguin include the El Niño phenomenon, fisheries, industrial development, human presence, habitat disturbance, and feral species. When Humboldt penguins see, hear, or smell that humans are near, they freak out. They are considered the most timid species of all penguins because they react to humans' presence from just 150 meters away (492.12 feet).

The feral animals are usually feral cats and dogs that feed on the chick, juvenile, and adult penguins. Other animals found in central Chile that are considered a threat to the Humboldt penguin even if they do not prey on the penguins are European rabbits and Norway rats. The European rabbits tend only to eat the vegetation where the Humboldt penguins reside.

Norway rats, however, feed off the vegetation and the eggs that are left unattended. Black rats in Chile also prey on the eggs for a source of their food. Feral goats were also introduced to the Puñihuil Islands; they had a drastic effect on the Humboldt penguins' population. This is because they ravaged the vegetation from the island. Penguins do not eat grass and vegetation in their diet, but they use it to make their nest during the breeding season.

These are just a few examples of the threats that the Humboldt penguins face that are not always predators. This could be why the IUCN has listed them as vulnerable to extinction, especially since they were once hunted. In Chile, they placed a 30-year ban on the hunting of Humboldt penguins in 1995. And in 2010, the U.S. Endangered Species Act granted protection for the Chile and Peru penguin populations.

Humboldt penguins can also be found in zoos. These places include the United States, India, Japan, the United Kingdom, Germany, and Ireland. Zoos housing the Humboldt penguins can also be found in other locations. During 2012 in the Tokyo Sea Life Park, there were 153 penguins, and one of them, who was not given a name but is known by his/her number, which is 337, managed to escape.

The penguin somehow climbed over a 4 meter (13.1 feet) high wall and passed through what would seem like a painful barbed wire fence. He/she survived in the Tokyo Bay for 82 days after escaping from the Sea Life Park. Zookeepers managed to capture the penguin towards the end of May of that year.

Lesson 90: The Galapagos Penguins

Galapagos penguins are the second smallest penguin with an average height of 19 inches and an average weight of 5.5 pounds. About 90 percent of the Galapagos penguins live on the west coast of Isabela Island and Fernandina Island. Due to Isabela's northern tip crossing into the north half of the equator, this makes the Galapagos penguin the only penguin known to geographically live in the Northern Hemisphere. Their diet is of small schooling fish such as mullet and sardines.

They forage during the daytime and return to their breeding grounds at night. Galapagos penguins tend not to venture too far from their breeding grounds due to the cold, nutrient-rich currents called the Cromwell Current and the Humboldt Current that they use to get their food. These penguins are endangered, with fewer than 1,000 breeding pairs in the world. Even with this fact, the Galapagos penguin mates for life.

The times their nests are seen are between May and January. A Bermudian naturalist named Louis L. Mowbray was the first to breed Galapagos penguins in captivity successfully. Due to their small size, Galapagos penguins have many predators and threats. Their predators are crabs, snakes, cats, Galapagos Hawks, dogs, rice rats, and short-eared owls on land.

While in the ocean, they face threats from sharks, fur seals, and sea lions. They face threats from humans as well, be it intended or accidental, most involving oil spills. Another devastating and unstoppable threat to the Galapagos penguins is nature, whether unreliable food sources and shortages or volcanic activity. Humans can't stop the natural threats to Galapagos penguins, but human threats can be stopped.

The conservation status of the Galapagos penguins is endangered. One reason which is the most common reason known to affect the Galapagos penguins is that available nesting areas that existed several years ago are now flooded due to the water rising from global warming. The El Niño phenomenon also has affected the Galapagos penguins just as much as the Humboldt penguins.

Pollution caused oil spills, human inference, and predation are just a few more reasons the Galapagos penguins are endangered. Humans harm penguins, even if it is accidental. It could be something as small as fishing the same area every day for a year, or even something as big as an oil ship starts leaking oil near where the penguins live and breed.

Small populations of Galapagos penguins reside in different parts near the equator including, Floreana, Bartolomé, Santiago, and northern Santa Cruz. They even live at the tip of the northern half of the island known as Isabela. Because the northern part of Isabela crosses the equator into the northern hemisphere, the Galapagos penguin is the only penguin species to live in the northern hemisphere naturally. Although there are small populations of Galapagos penguins throughout South America, precisely 90 percent live in the Fernandina and Isabela Islands.

Their diet consists mainly of schooling fish that are small fish such as mullet and sardines. Crustaceans are an occasional food source. Galapagos penguins are like the rest of the penguin species and tend to eat more during certain times of the year, such as molting and breeding seasons.

The temperature in and around the Galapagos is usually between 59 and 82 °F. which makes this location ideal for incubating eggs. Though they wouldn't intentionally leave the nest unattended, they probably could, and the eggs would still be kept warm for a time. When the ocean's surface temperature is below 77 °F, this is usually the time Galapagos penguins begin breeding.

The Galapagos penguins are also considered endangered because there are less than 1,000 sexually mature breeding pairs left in the world. Yes, while each pair can have two eggs in a single clutch and could have a second clutch, only one chick from a clutch of two is expected to survive. While having a second clutch is possible, it doesn't happen often and the reason a second clutch is needed is usually that the first clutch of eggs failed.

In 2004 the estimated population number of at least 1,500 was estimated during a survey done by Charles Darwin Research Station. And an alarming decrease in the population of surprisingly over 70 percent during the 1980s. The Galapagos penguins are the rarest species to live on Earth today; many believe that this species belongs to the yellow-eyed penguins though they have a higher population size. When and if the Galapagos penguins go extinct, then the rarest penguin's title will go to yellow-eyed penguin.

Lesson 91: The Southern Ocean Islands Have Three Species of Penguins

The islands in the Southern Oceans include Trinity Island, D'Urville Island, Reid Island, Wednesday Island, Somerville Island, Saddle Island, Link Island, Ewing Island, and many others. There are three species of penguins in the Southern Ocean Islands: the Macaroni Penguin, the Southern Rockhopper, and the Northern Rockhopper. These penguins are all a part of the crested penguin classification.

Lesson 92: The Macaroni Penguin

Macaroni penguins' diets involve small fish and cephalopods but mainly krill and other varieties of crustaceans. The adult penguins are, on average, 28 inches tall, weighing an average of 12 pounds. Macaroni penguins are known for their distinctive yellow crest on their heads, leaving some people referring it to a noodle like look. Like all other penguins species, these penguins molt once a year, having to stay ashore during the 3-4-week period of molting.

The Macaroni penguin is believed to have about a minimum of 11.8 million individual penguins, even with their numbers decreasing since the mid-1970s. They are one of six or so penguins in the genus

Eudyptes, commonly referred to as the crested penguins. After molting, their black plumage tends to have a blueish shine due to being new, yet before molting when feathers are old, they have a brownish tinge to them.

In November breeding, the females produce a clutch of two eggs. In most clutches of eggs, the second egg is the biggest, so the first egg will be kicked from the nest, rarely will the breeding couple keep both eggs and raise them. At about 11 weeks after the young penguin hatches, they are fully independent to leave the nest and forage on their own.

Some authorities or most likely researchers/specialists believe the macaroni penguins and royal penguins to be of a single breed instead of two different breeds due to how closely related they are. Male and female macaroni penguins look quite similar to each other. The only differences are the male penguins are bigger and stronger (like human males) with a longer, bigger bill size.

Though there are believed to have around a minimum of 11.8 million macaroni penguins, they have still been listed as vulnerable by the International Union for Conservation of Nature. This breed eats more sea creatures of their diet yearly than any other seabird out there.

The scientific name for macaroni penguins, Eudyptes Chrysolophus, comes from the Ancient Greek language. 'Eu' in Ancient Greek means good while 'dyptes' means diver, so the first word of the genus, Eudyptes, literally means 'good diver'. The second word of the genus means 'golden crest' due to the word chrysolophus being broken into two words. 'Chryse' means golden, while 'lophus' translates into crest.

There is a quick fact that I found to be a unique fact about not just the macaroni penguins but also about the song "Yankee Doodle." That fact is that during the 18th-century, England had a style called Maccaronism. This meant people wore flamboyant ornamentation upon their heads.

Just a part of the song leads me to believe that the flamboyant item is typically on a hat or headband of some sort. The part I am referring to is "Yankee Doodle went to town. A-riding on a pony, stuck a feather in his cap. And called it macaroni."

Just like most penguins, the macaroni penguins are a very social bird. They use visual displays and vocal displays during their interactions. They also try to "unseat" each other during nest season when they become frustrated with their neighbor penguin. Male penguins do this by locking each other's bills together and wrestling, trying to knock one or the other off their nests. Doing this is called 'bill-jousting,' and they also flap their wings while trying to peck at each other.

Lesson 93: The Southern Rockhopper Penguin

The Southern Rockhopper penguin is considered to be the smallest penguin that is yellow-crested in the Eudyptes genus. They weigh 4.4-7.5 pounds, and they grow to at least 18-23 inches. This penguin has slate-grey feathers on the penguin's upperparts with a bright-yellow crest above their eyes that some people like to think of as the penguin's eyebrows. They have red eyes with more yellow feathers showing behind their eyes.

Between 1987 and 1988, an Australian National Research Expedition reported the Rockhopper penguins interbreeding with the Macaroni penguins, having recorded three hybrids. Their diet consists mainly of crustaceans, but they also feed on mollusks, octopus, plankton, cuttlefish, squid, and lantern fish.

Breeding season for these penguins begins in September and ends in November with two eggs laid, and usually only one is incubated. Both species of Rockhopper penguins got their name from their hopping movements as they tend to hop across rocky surfaces and leap over cracks in the ground.

The full scientific name for the southern rockhopper penguin is Eudyptes chrysocome. We know that Eudyptes in Ancient Greek translates to "good diver," but little can be found (at least be me) about what "chrysocome" means in Ancient Greek. There are two subspecies of the southern rockhopper, and their scientific names are Eudyptes chrysocome chrysocome and Eudyptes chrysocome filholi.

The two subspecies are known as the western rockhopper and the eastern rockhopper penguins. As you may have guessed, Southern Rockhopper penguins are related to the northern rockhopper penguins and are also agreed to be one species. Still, they are also related to the macaroni and royal penguins. There are also three hybrid species meaning the southern rockhopper penguins and the macaroni penguins have been recorded interbreeding during the Australian National Antarctic Research Expedition of 1987-88.

The southern rockhopper penguins' global population is around 1 million pairs, so at least 2 million individual penguins. These penguins' diet is mainly crustaceans, though they do feed on cuttlefish, lanternfish, krill, octopus, plankton, squid, and mollusks.

A rockhopper penguin in the Bergen Aquarium in Norway lived in captivity until he passed away in October 2003. His name was Rocky, and he lived to be 29 years and four months old. It is believed that he was possibly the eldest penguin to date.

While being highly sociable penguins, they are also believed to be one of the most aggressive. This can be proven just because they can fight each other while incubating their eggs during the nesting season. Watching these penguins jump over rocks and cracks is the closest thing anyone will get to see as penguins' flying'.

The other crested penguins in the Eudyptes genus hop around on and over rocks and cracks in the ground. Rockhopper penguins can be in places that were once visited by whalers and explorers during breaks they would take. The New Zealand region is where this took place and when their behavior was first discovered.

Lesson 94: Northern Rockhopper Penguin

In 2009 a study showed that the population of Northern Rockhopper penguins had decreased since the 1950s by 90 percent, marking these penguins as endangered. Northern Rockhopper penguins breed on the Tristan da Cunha and Gough Islands in the south Atlantic Ocean. Their diet is mainly krill and other crustaceans, but they also feed on fish, squid, and octopus.

During the breeding season, the Northern Rockhopper penguin shows that they favor future reproduction by feeding on zooplankton and switch to feeding on fish. They have a lifespan of 9-12 years, which is kind of short compared to other penguins.

These penguins weigh on average 6.6 pounds and are 20.4-21.6 inches tall on average. Like the Southern Rockhopper, the Northern Rockhopper has yellow plumes on the sides of their head, but the Northern Rockhopper penguins' plumes are longer in comparison.

The genus of the northern rockhopper penguins is called Eudyptes moseleyi. They are also known as the Moseley's penguin. They are endangered as a 2009 study has shown a 90 percent decrease in population since the 1950s.

The northern rockhopper penguins feed mostly on krill and other crustaceans, but they also eat small fish, octopus, and squid. They tend to eat more during the breeding season, as do most penguins, so they can last a while longer during the incubation season even though they take turns.

When it comes to breeding grounds and areas, they usually range from inland, sea level, and even cliff sides. The northern rockhoppers show that they favor their future reproduction and offspring by eating zooplankton then switching to fish during the breeding season.

The population for the northern rockhoppers has not been counted or kept track of since the 1990s. To be more exact, since 1993, and at that time, their numbers were around 1,131,998 individual penguins. There was a decrease of at least 2.7 percent each year since the 1950s, which almost equates to 100 penguins dying every day.

On the 16th of March, during the year 2011, an oil rig named MS Oliva scraped against high ground, most likely during a low tide on Nightingale Island where they spilled tons of heavy crude oil into the sea. The crew had to be recused because the freighter broke apart as it ran aground.

As the rig broke apart, spilling the oil, it began surrounding the island and endangered the rockhopper penguins and other sea life that lived there. Due to Nightingale Island having no freshwater, the northern rockhopper penguins had to be moved to Tristan da Cunha for freshwater and cleansing to save the penguins.

Lesson 95: Africa Has One Species of Penguin

In Africa, there is only one breed of penguin, and that penguin is the African Penguin. It is a species of penguin that stays and lives in southern African waters. This penguin also goes by the names Cape penguin or the South African Penguin. The African penguin belongs to the genus Spheniscus.

Lesson 96: The African Penguin

African penguins have distinctive characteristics of pink skin patches above their eyes. This penguin feeds primarily on squid and fish in the African waters. They weigh 4.9-7.7 pounds measuring in at 24-28 inches tall.

These penguins were quite numerous in the past, but they have become endangered due to several threats to these penguins. Only found in Africa, these penguins live on 24 islands near Port Elizabeth, South Africa.

Their presence in between Namibia and Algoa Bay gave the Penguin Islands their name. These penguins are classified as endangered because around the 20th century, only 10 percent of the species remained. Ecologists believe that by 2026 African penguins will be extinct in the wild.

The diet of African penguins includes pelagic and marine invertebrates, consuming at least 1.1 pounds of food per day. African penguins are monogamous, and pairs return to the same breeding site each year.

Monogamous meaning the African penguin chooses one mate and stays with them for life. It appears they also like routine, seeing as how they return to the same breeding site every year.

I just found out that the African penguins are non-aggressive, but the young can be very belligerent. They make a call that is unique to them. It sounds as if a donkey was "braying" in a colony of African penguins.

But the most interesting thing I found out about this penguin is that because of the sound the young ones make, they can be known by the name of the "Jackass Penguin," seeing as that is what donkeys are called.

The genus for the Cape penguin, also known as the African penguin, is Spheniscus demersus. They are an endangered species of penguins, as quite a few of them are. The African penguins are also called Cape penguins because they can be found in Cape Town, which is in South Africa.

The bright pink area above their eyes is what helps these penguins still cool. It is a thermoregulation gland. This means that once the penguin begins to get too warm, their body sends blood into these glands, which is then cooled down by the air and the nice breeze they most likely receive.

The Ancient Greek-Latin translation of the genus Spheniscus demersus is 'wedge plunging.' Taking the word sphen and translating it into wedge while taking the word demersus and translating it from Latin into plunging.

The African penguins resemble three other penguins, the Humboldt, Galapagos, and the Magellanic penguins. And due to their resemblance, many believe they are all related to one another, which could make sense seeing as they look quite alike.

African penguins live on 24 islands ranging from Algoa Bay and Namibia around Port Elizabeth in South Africa, even though, as of 2018, these penguins' population is 50,000 penguins left and constantly decreasing.

Chapter Review

This chapter is about the different breeds of penguins, and there are five facts from this chapter that I find the most interesting. Fact number one that I find the most interesting in this chapter is that there is a penguin with yellow eyes, and they are named after their eye coloration.

A second fact I found the most interesting is that penguins are a monogamous bird. They mate with one penguin for their entire life. The third fact is that one penguin species is called the Little Blue/Fairy penguin. I loved finding out about the Little Blue/Fairy penguin.

Fact number four that I find interesting is that the African penguins could also be known as the "Jackass Penguin" because of the young penguins' call. And the final fact from this chapter, fact number five, is the Galapagos penguin being the only penguin to live close enough to the Northern Hemisphere. They are considered the only penguin who lives in the wild to live in the Northern Hemisphere.

Chapter 12: Predators of Penguins

Penguins have many predators. Some they can run away from, and some they cannot. Most of these predators are typical for all penguins, but some penguins become prey to uncommon predators due to their size. In this chapter, we will discuss all the common predators and a few of the uncommon ones.

Lesson 97: Sharks

Sharks are not the main predator to penguins, but they will hunt them when necessary. Yes, sharks are a predator to many oceans bound creatures. Sharks eat penguins if they cannot find any other food, but one penguin would not be enough to make a shark full.

Lesson 98: Leopard Seals

Now, this predator is one that penguins are always on the lookout for. The leopard seal preys on many of the penguin species, especially the Emperor penguins. These seals have a very strategic hunting pattern. They can attack penguins on land and in the water.

They have been known to attack penguins on both sides. Meaning the attack from the left or right heading straight for the penguins they are hunting. While on land, they cannot move as agilely as penguins, yet they will chase them away. They chase penguins on land, hoping that it will become scared and nervous enough to jump into the water.

Being in the water is the leopard seals' strong suit. With the shapes of their bodies being that of a torpedo, they can move more elegantly and capture the penguin it is hunting almost every time. When searching for food, they scan the horizon looking for any signs of movement just like most predators, while also sniffing the air to find any scents to follow.

Lesson 99: Fur Seals

Fur seals are like leopard seals to me because they have a diet that includes penguins from time to time. They do tend to eat penguins. However, according to the BBC website, all the way from back in 2014, fur seals have been spotted trying to have sex with the penguins instead. So, fur seals and leopard seals are entirely different in that aspect.

According to the BBC website, the fur seals that try having sex with penguins tend to be the male fur seals. I know I am meant to discuss how the fur seal is a predator to penguins, but this fact is one of the only points that stand out entirely in my face when researching fur seals preying on penguins.

Lesson 100: Whales

Typically, the only whale to go after any penguin is the killer whale, also known as the Orca. These whales tend to have a diet that includes penguins more because a penguin or two make them full faster than eating several dozen fish.

Though they are like sharks and are not usually found in areas where there are many penguins, they will choose to eat a penguin before a shark will, however. Killer whales found in the hunting grounds of penguins are there typically because their primary food source has traveled away from the regular spot killer whales' feed.

Lesson 101: Leopards

A leopard is not a common predator for penguins, as they cannot live in the Antarctic and Sub-Antarctic Islands. So, the only penguin that has to deal with leopards as a predator is the African penguin.

Yes, I know all penguins have to protect themselves from leopard seals, but we aren't talking about leopard seals in this lesson. I'm talking about the big spotted cat that lives in Africa right alongside the African penguin.

No, penguins are not their primary source of food, but there have been debates about the conservation of African penguins due to leopards eating them. Some say they shouldn't allow this big cat to eat these rare penguins, while others argue that the leopard is an even rarer creature locally in Africa.

Lesson 102: Humans

Now humans. We all know there are many things we do wrong as a species and this includes not being more careful of how we treat the animals on our beautiful planet. How are humans' predators to penguins, you may ask? During the first few early expeditions for penguin research, the meals when landing and researching them were fresh penguin meat.

This is a fact due to the rationing of food supply, and, most likely, the food researchers did bring would end up going bad because of poor refrigeration. So, yes, at one point in time, people ate penguins. Do they still eat penguins?

Not as many people eat penguins as there used to be. Anthropologists once believed that the native people of South America, New Zealand, and Australia hunted penguins as a form of their diet. But now penguins are not hunted by humans as much. Most likely, due to conservation acts placed around each penguin breed as their numbers are dropping by the year, maybe even by the day.

Lesson 103: Rice Rats

Rice rats are one of the uncommon predators for penguins. The main penguin breed that is hunted by this predator is the Galapagos penguins. To my surprise, this rat is not any bigger than the common rat you could find in New York.

With a length from head to toe of at least 9 to 20 centimeters, it comes as a big surprise to me that this rat could be a predator to a decently more giant penguin. Seeing as these rats weigh on average between 40 and 80 grams, I don't understand how they can even eat a whole Galapagos penguin.

Having discussed the size of this predatory rat, let's talk about where they can be found. Seeing as they can hunt the Galapagos penguin, they would have to live around the Galapagos Islands to find the penguins. These rats live in the southern parts of North America and the northern regions of South America.

Lesson 104: Dogs

Dogs are another predator that is not a common one for all penguins. These predators go for the Little Blue penguin and Galapagos penguin. It is not as common anymore for dogs to go after either of these penguins seeing as they have to live in these parts of the world to hunt them.

There is proof that dogs and penguins can live in peace with one another. In Warrnambool, a Victorian coastal town on a small island, some dogs shepherd the Fairy penguins. These dogs are called Maremma Sheepdogs. And now, instead of dogs attacking and eating penguins, they are protecting them, even from the predator we will discuss next, foxes.

Lesson 105: Foxes

Foxes are an uncommon predator and only go after one penguin species, the Fairy penguins. Due to their small size and stature, the Fairy penguins have many predators, including one in the ocean and mostly involving the ones on land.

Foxes hunt the Fairy penguins because they live in the same area as them. But since the Maremma Sheepdogs began protecting the Fairy penguin, these foxes have since slowed down hunting them. The species of fox that almost wiped out an entire colony of Fairy penguins was the red fox.

They killed every single one of the Fairy penguins on Middle Island except for four of them. Middle Island is off Australia's coast and used to be home to hundreds of Fairy penguins until the red fox came to the island from the mainland and almost entirely wiped them out.

Lesson 106: Cats

Cats are predators to lots of birds, so would it come as a surprise if they hunted penguins too? Penguins are, after all, just like any other bird. Except most of them are bigger, slower, and none of them can fly.

The penguins that are hunted by cats are the Galapagos penguins and the Fairy penguins. This is due to its size. The Fairy penguin is the smallest penguin in the world, and the Galapagos penguin is the second smallest. The Fairy penguin does not get any bigger than 14 inches tall, and the Galapagos penguins only reach 21 inches tall at maximum.

So, with that being said, I could see how a cat who is born and raised in the wild could go after a penguin, especially if they have not eaten in a few days. But seeing a cat go after, say, an Emperor penguin, nope, I can't see that happening; they are too big.

Lesson 107: Reptiles

Now you wouldn't expect to see a reptile eating a penguin, well at least I wouldn't. But when you think about what animals are reptiles, it starts to make more sense how a reptile can eat penguins.

To me, reptiles are just lizards and snakes. Well, let's think about it for a second. A crocodile is a reptile, and so are alligators. Now we have to find out which one can catch and eat a penguin due to being on the same continent as penguins. Well, crocodiles live in

Africa, Australia, Asia, and both North and South America.

So, check, crocodiles can hunt penguins, but what about alligators. After researching alligators to find out if they hunt penguins, I discovered that the only places in the entire world that alligators have been found are North America and China. So no, alligators do not hunt penguins.

Chapter Review

The five facts from this chapter are, 'fur seals can be predators towards penguins but they have more recently been seen trying to mate with them,' 'dogs used to hunt penguins now they protect them,' 'reptiles can hunt penguins,' 'sharks tend not to eat penguins as much as I thought,' 'rice rats are a type of rat that hunt penguins.'

I will start with the last fact for fact number one because that is the craziest sounding thing to me. Rice rats from subtropical regions near South America can hunt penguins. More specifically, the Galapagos penguin. I find this fact astonishing because I cannot wrap my head around the fact that a rat can eat a penguin.

Anyhow moving on to fact number two, dogs used to hunt penguins. Now instead of hunting them, they protect them from other predators. The Maremma Sheepdogs protect and shepherd Fairy penguins from foxes who tend to hunt these penguins just as the dogs did. Fact number three that I found interesting is that sharks do not hunt or eat penguins as much as I thought they would. Sharks tend to stay away from eating penguins as part of their diet, being the fact that it would take more than one penguin to make a shark full, and usually, penguins break off from their fishing parties to scavenger for food alone, and then they regroup.

Fact four that is also pretty crazy to me but interesting is the fur seals have hunted penguins, but in 2014 the male fur seals were spotted trying to mate with said penguins instead. This fact is just very strange yet interesting.

And the final fact for this chapter is reptiles can hunt penguins. To me, reptiles are always lizards and snakes. I always forget that crocodiles are reptiles too. Crocodiles can hunt penguins just as sharks can, but there aren't many articles or records of crocodiles eating penguins.

Crocodiles chasing penguins, yes, eating them? I have not found anything yet, even though they live in the same regions as some penguins. Snakes and lizards do eat penguins, though. Lizards go after Fairy penguins, and snakes go after Galapagos penguins.

Conclusion

As we wrap up our 101+ lessons about penguins, why don't we look back on a few lessons? One lesson I would like to look back on the frequently asked questions section of our guide. Finding the answers to questions about penguins is the finest part of a guide (to me anyhow). Asking questions about penguins is the best way to learn about them in the order you want to learn.

A second lesson for us to look back on during this guide is there are multiple places in the world to see penguins. Whether you pay to see penguins at the zoo or aquarium or visit them in their natural habitat in the wild for free, visiting where penguins are is also educational, so you will be able to view penguins being themselves even in zoos and aquariums.

The third and final lesson of our wrap up of the 101+ lessons about penguins guide is there are multiple species of penguins. Many believe there are 18 different species, while others think they're up to as many as 20 species of penguins. Though, as we can see from the guide, I have done the research and only found 18 species of penguins, which are still many breeds.

In conclusion, there are many facts about penguins. Researchers are finding out more information every day. I hope you have enjoyed reading this guide as much I have enjoyed making it for all of us penguin enthusiasts. Long live the penguins!

About the Expert

Skylar Isaac has loved penguins since she was about four years old. She grew up knowing many fun things about penguins and had always wanted to learn more and teach her friends. Learning about penguins has been a passion of Skylar's ever since she discovered more than one penguin species. She first noticed there were different breeds of penguins since childhood by watching movies and playing video games. Even in junior high, Skylar had a love for penguins that never seemed to die down. Her passion for penguins only grew fonder the more she learned about penguins as a whole and the individual species. Skylar hopes that writing this guide will educate people and entertain them with new lessons about penguins that they may never have known in the past. She is now a freelance writer who hopes to captivate people to use their imagination and see themselves in each fascinating story and informative guide through her writing.

HowExpert publishes quick 'how to' guides on all topics from A to Z by everyday experts. Visit HowExpert.com to learn more.

Recommended Resources

- HowExpert.com – Quick 'How To' Guides on All Topics from A to Z by Everyday Experts.
- HowExpert.com/free – Free HowExpert Email Newsletter.
- HowExpert.com/books – HowExpert Books
- HowExpert.com/courses – HowExpert Courses
- HowExpert.com/clothing – HowExpert Clothing
- HowExpert.com/membership – HowExpert Membership Site
- HowExpert.com/affiliates – HowExpert Affiliate Program
- HowExpert.com/jobs – HowExpert Jobs
- HowExpert.com/writers – Write About Your #1 Passion/Knowledge/Expertise & Become a HowExpert Author.
- HowExpert.com/resources – Additional HowExpert Recommended Resources
- YouTube.com/HowExpert – Subscribe to HowExpert YouTube.
- Instagram.com/HowExpert – Follow HowExpert on Instagram.
- Facebook.com/HowExpert – Follow HowExpert on Facebook.

Printed in Great Britain
by Amazon